Integrated Electronics

MODERN ELECTRICAL
STUDIES

A Series Edited by
Professor G. D. SIMS

Head of Department of Electronics,
University of Southampton

Integrated Electronics

by K. J. DEAN B.Sc.

*Head of the Department of
Science and Electrical Engineering,
Letchworth College of Technology*

CHAPMAN AND HALL LTD
11 NEW FETTER LANE LONDON EC4

First published 1967
© *K. J. Dean* 1967
Printed in Great Britain by
Butler & Tanner Ltd
Frome and London

Contents

Modified, directly coupled transistor logic. Resistor–capacitor transistor logic. Diode–transistor logic. Transistor–transistor logic. Current–mode logic. Complementary transistor logic. FET logic elements. Summary

Plates 1–6 appear between pages 12 and 13

Preface

One of the current problems we face today is to avoid training for obsolescence. Education always embraces training for industry, and in electronics we have now become used to the changing industrial pattern. First we learnt about valves, then alloy junction transistors, next planar transistors, and now integrated circuits.

This series, *Modern Electrical Studies*, was envisaged to assist in formal education and in furthering the natural desire of electrical and electronics engineers to keep abreast of recent developments. It is to be hoped that this book will be characteristic of the series.

In this book, the fundamentals of thin-film and silicon integrated electronic circuits have been carefully developed, but not from the point of view of the manufacturer of such circuits, for the majority of us will never make a single integrated circuit. We are much more interested in their uses and limitations. However, it is important for the user to know a certain amount about manufacturing methods and design philosophies in order to appreciate where limitations occur and the reasons for their occurrence. It is also of value in discriminating between the apparently similar circuits which are available and the rival claims of manufacturers.

It is not possible in a book of this size to write a comprehensive electronics textbook. Here the new electronics is examined, and one has to rely on the reader being familiar with much that has gone before. The purpose of this book is to modify that knowledge in the light of these new developments.

Some readers would perhaps have preferred to find more information on certain topics, such as the merits of various encapsulation methods or the testing of integrated circuits. On others, such as noise immunity, there is a great deal of work still to be done. I have been conscious that no selection of topics would please everyone, and, if it seems that my selection tends to emphasise the digital applications of integrated electronics, I can only point out that it is in precisely this field that most headway has been made.

I have included a number of aspects of systems design which I believe to be new, and have given, in some detail, examples of typical design problems which illustrate some of the points which have been discussed.

This book should, therefore, be of value to all those electronics engineers who are willing to make terms with change, whether they be graduates or undergraduates or Higher National Diploma students at our Colleges of Technology.

The co-operation of a number of manufacturers and users of integrated circuits has been of very great help and their generosity has made my task easier. I also wish to acknowledge with thanks the work of members of the staff of Letchworth College of Technology in the preparation of the photographic plates in this book.

K. J. DEAN

Glossary

A glossary of some common terms in the technology of integrated electronics.

Channel A region of doped semiconductor with a large length-to-width ratio. p-channel and n-channel devices exist, depending on the nature of the carriers which are present.

Dissipation This is a measure of the power dissipated by a circuit, and hence of the heat which must be removed from it. It is commonly the case that circuits with long propagation delays dissipate less power than faster circuits.

Enhancement mode A mode of operation of MOS transistors in which the field due to the gate electrode makes more carriers available to take part in conduction.

Epitaxy A technique in which a thin layer is formed on a silicon chip. The epitaxial layer has the same crystal structure as the material on which it is formed, but is usually of higher resistivity. In it, transistors and other circuit elements can be formed by selective diffusion.

Fan-out This is the number of similar elements which can be connected to the output of an element. However, some manufacturers have attempted to rationalise their systems by specifying a standard load, and quoting the rationalised fan-out in terms of this load. They also state the load imposed by each of the elements in their range in these terms. Hence, the rationalised fan-out of an element, divided by the input load number, gives the fan-out of that element to a number of other elements, similar to each other.

Field effect A potential difference between an insulated electrode or a reverse-biased junction and a doped semiconductor region causes an electric field, which results in a change in the number of free carriers available to take part in conduction in the region. The effect is most marked when the conduction takes place in a narrow channel in the field.

Hybrid integrated circuit An integrated circuit which uses both thin-film and silicon chip techniques for the circuit elements.

Integrated circuit A circuit which is so constructed as to be considered as an indivisible whole, both for use and for servicing. (See also silicon integrated circuit and thin-film integrated circuit.)

Land A part of a silicon integrated circuit held at such a potential that circuit elements diffused into it can easily be isolated from other elements in the circuit by reverse bias of the land to the substrate in which it is formed.

Microelectronics The technology of the fabrication and the applications of highly miniaturised electronic circuits. A microelectronic circuit is one in which the packing density of circuit elements is greater than about three per cubic centimetre.

Monolithic circuit An integrated circuit which uses either thin-film or silicon chip techniques for both active and passive elements, but not a mixture of both of these. However, the term is more usually reserved for silicon chip construction.

Multi-chip circuit A circuit in which individual elements or groups of elements are fabricated on individual chips or substrates which are then interconnected to form a complete circuit.

Noise immunity The noise immunity of a circuit is usually expressed in volts, but a lower noise immunity can be tolerated for a low impedance circuit than for one with a higher impedance. Recent developments have been aimed at specifying noise immunity in terms of charge.

Parasitic plague When a transistor is formed in a silicon layer whose doping is different from that of the adjacent layer of the transistor, a four-layer device is formed. This device is considered as consisting of the desired transistor in conjunction with the parasitic transistor, whose current gain should be kept low. This parasite may degrade the performance of the silicon integrated circuit. This is parasitic plague.

Planar A transistor or integrated circuit may be called planar if it is wholly constructed within the epitaxial layer which is grown on the substrate of a silicon chip or close to the surface of a chip if there is no epitaxial layer. Silicon integrated circuits were not developed until the planar epitaxial process had become established. They owe their development very largely to this process.

Propagation delay This is a measure of the time taken for a change in input level to an element to appear as a change in its output level. Since the direction of the change may affect the propagation delay, it is usually stated as the mean of the delays for positive-going and for negative-going input changes. Particularly where this term is applied to digital circuits, it is found to be a function of the fan-out (q.v.) of the element, increasing with fan-out. However, the rate of increase varies very much from one type of element to another.

Purple plague A purple, intermetallic compound, $AuAl_2$, is formed when gold wires are bonded to aluminium metallised surfaces. It is responsible for high-resistivity joints and fractures where the wires are bonded. In the presence of silicon, a more virulent form, sometimes called black death, is formed. The term 'purple plague' is commonly applied to both of these.

Silicon integrated circuit An integrated circuit produced on one or more silicon chips and which is a functional unit without the use of additional components. This is somewhat loosely interpreted in the case of operational amplifiers.

Thin-film integrated circuit An integrated circuit produced by the deposition of thin films on a single substrate. Where the deposition is produced by evaporation or sputtering, a genuine, thin-film circuit is produced, but, where silk-screen printing and chemical deposition are used, it may be preferable to regard the circuit as a thick-film circuit, in order to distinguish it from those produced by vacuum techniques. These terms usually apply to the passive circuit elements only, transistors and diodes being subsequently added.

CHAPTER 1

The Development of the
Alloy Junction Transistor

Introduction

The development of the transistor is probably the single factor which has had the greatest effect on the design of electronic circuitry since the second world war. For some time, it seemed that the transistor would be developed in the same way as the thermionic triode a decade or so previously. Manufacturers strove for higher gains and greater frequency response. However, in pursuing these aims, new manufacturing techniques were discovered, and the accompanying research effort led to new devices also. Thus, the tunnel diode and the field effect transistor, amongst others, were added to the range of semiconductor devices.

It was now becoming apparent that the transistor was not to be treated just as a replacement for the valve in a conventional circuit, for its greatly smaller size led manufacturers to look more closely at the circuit components, resistors, capacitors, and the like, with which it was associated. This was not only on account of the space reduction involved, but it was hoped that increased reliability could be obtained if these components could be fabricated as a whole, rather than interconnecting individually made components. This hope was later justified by results.

Thus, the transistor is seen, not as an end in itself, but as a stage in the development of microminiature circuits of high reliability. Events have also shown that microelectronic circuits have brought about a reduction in the size of, say, an amplifier, of a similar order to that when valve circuits were first transistorised. There is, on the other hand, a price to be paid for these advantages. Research is expensive, for it is not immediately productive, and not all the development problems have yet been overcome.

1

This book is concerned with the applications of microelectronic circuits. In the early days of the development of transistors, much was written about the manufacture of these devices and relatively little about their use in circuitry. The same thing was true of many of the transistor courses in Colleges of Technology at that time. A similar situation seems to apply today in the field of microminiature circuitry. However, it should not be thought that this is an argument for an explanation of circuitry which is not based on an adequate understanding of the behaviour of the active devices. In this book, there will be some discussion of the phenomenon of semiconduction and transistor action, in order that those facts may be established which are essential to later argument. Some consideration will also be given to the design and construction of microminiature circuits, so that, when the uses of these circuits are discussed, the reader will be presented with sufficient information to assess which techniques are most likely to lead him to the best solutions of the design problems with which he is confronted. In this way, it is hoped to present a balanced picture of microminiaturisation, in which the problems of device design are outlined, and their bearing on system design is explained.

Conduction in Semiconductors
Semiconductors are substances with resistivities between those of good conductors, such as copper, and insulators, such as glass. They frequently have large, negative temperature coefficients of resistance, and some form of rectifier action is frequently associated with them. Nowadays, it is possible to explain semiconduction in terms of the band theory of solids, in which the permitted energy levels of valence and conduction electrons exhibit a band gap. In the case of insulators, this energy gap is large, while in conductors no such gap exists. Semiconductors have a band gap of the order of 1 electron-volt. To establish such a theory, experiments had to be carried out on extremely pure semiconductors. Some of the phenomena associated with semiconductors have been known for many years, but it was not until techniques became available for the production of materials having either high purity, or carefully regulated, known impurities that it became possible to examine them critically,

and to put forward successfully a theory to explain their behaviour. Two of the first semiconductors to be prepared in this way were germanium and silicon. The methods used, those of crystal pulling and zone refining, not only made it possible to reduce impurities to below one part in 10^9, but also produced a monocrystalline structure. Hence, throughout the ingot there was a uniform lattice structure of atomic sites with a minimum number of lattice defects. This monocrystalline formation has been found to be an essential requirement in semiconductor devices.

Once the pure or *intrinsic* material has been produced, it is possible to add controlled quantities of impurities to it. Thus, a trace of an impurity, such as arsenic, which is pentavalent, noticeably affects the behaviour of the material. If the quantity of the impurity is very small, say one part in 10^8, so that the atoms of the impurity can be considered to be isolated in the host material, then atoms of impurity will have no noticeable affect on one another, and will take their place in the crystal lattice of the tetravalent semiconductor. Since we have a pentavalent atom in a tetravalent structure, there is a free electron available to take part in conduction for every impurity atom present. This conduction is extrinsic or *impurity* conduction.

Thus, in this case, the intrinsic material has been doped with arsenic, donating electrons to take part in conduction, so forming an *n-type* semiconductor. In this n-type material, two types of conduction take place. There is the intrinsic conduction which rises rapidly with increasing temperature, and the *impurity conduction* of electrons (also called n-type carriers) which is not nearly so much affected by temperature. We shall be particularly interested in the case where the temperature is sufficiently low for the impurity conduction to be some orders greater than the intrinsic conduction. This is the case at room temperature. Thus, typically, we shall be concerned with impurity currents of the order of a few milliamps and intrinsic currents which are often only a few nanoamps, or at most some tens of microamps.

Alternatively, it is possible to dope the intrinsic semiconductor with a trivalent impurity, such as aluminium. In this case, the isolated impurity atoms will each produce an incomplete bond in the lattice structure. This hole in the lattice can be filled by an electron from a neighbouring atom so that the hole moves as a positive charge through the crystal. A semiconductor doped in this way is said to be a p-type material, and again two forms of conduction take place in it. As before, intrinsic conduction is kept small, while the impurity current consists of holes.

It should be noted that, when an e.m.f. is maintained across a slab of p-type material, the positive holes will move towards the negative terminal, being replaced from the positive terminal of the supply battery. Since an atom does not normally have a residual charge, the removal of a positive hole from it will leave the atomic site negatively charged. In the same way, an n-type material will contribute negative carriers, electrons, and their removal will leave positively charged atomic sites. In addition to this, intrinsic conduction still takes place. Thus, the addition of these impurities lowers the resistivity of the material, a heavily doped material having a much lower resistivity than a lightly doped one. However, the mechanism of current flow differs in the two cases in the way which has been described.

p–n **junction**
A particularly interesting result of doping occurs at the boundary between two, differently doped regions. Naturally occurring semi-conductors, such as galena, were used as rectifiers in early, crystal radio receivers. This rectifier action is due to the presence in the crystal of p–n junctions. A p–n junction is the boundary between p-type and n-type doped regions.

Figure 1.1 illustrates a p–n junction. It must be stressed that there is a continuous lattice structure across the junction, while the junction represents the plane which bounds an abrupt change of doping. Thus, if the p-type region is made negative with respect to the n-type region by applying a potential difference across the junction, the positive carriers will be removed from the p-type material (to the negative terminal) and cannot be replaced since there are no mobile positive carriers in the n-type region. Similarly, the negative carriers are removed from the n-type material. Thus, a potential barrier exists across the junction, and the current which flows is the intrinsic current. However, should the applied potential be increased, so that the p-type region is made more negative, the force acting on the mobile intrinsic carriers may become sufficiently large to cause atomic interactions or collisions, so releasing further carriers. Such an effect can rapidly become cumulative, resulting in a high current flow and, perhaps, sufficient power dissipation to cause diffusion of the impurities to take place at the junction, so destroying the discontinuity of doping there. Under these circumstances, the junction is said to be broken down.

Alternatively, if the p-type material is made positive with respect to the n-type region by reversing the potential of the supply, then the mobile p-carriers or holes are repelled, by the positive potential, into the n-type region. Similarly, the n-carriers, or electrons, there are passed into the p-type region. In both cases, there is nothing to prevent this current of holes and electrons continuing, since the carriers can easily be replaced by the battery which drives the current. Thus, there is a heavy current flow, and the junction is said to be forward

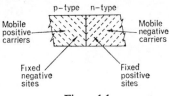

Figure 1.1

biased; whereas in the previous case, after the charges had been cleared from the vicinity of the junction, the current which flowed was only the very small intrinsic current and the junction was said to be reverse biased. Hence the junction current depends not only on the magnitude of the applied potential, but on its direction also. For this reason, the p–n junction is said to act as a rectifier.

The junction transistor

Figure 1.2 shows diagrammatically a section through a mono-crystalline slice of semiconductor. In the figure, the emitter region has been relatively heavily doped with an n-type impurity, so that it has the low resistance typically associated with an impure semiconductor. The p-type base region is relatively pure, so that when the base-emitter junction is forward biased the current consists chiefly of electrons from the emitter, and contains only few holes from the base. Careful design can ensure that this forward junction consists almost entirely of carriers from the emitter, a typical figure being 99·5 per cent., when the emitter efficiency is said to be 0·995.

Unlike the base–emitter junction, it is usual practice to reverse bias the base–collector junction. In an isolated junction of this kind, little current would normally flow, but the exception to this is when the base region is extremely thin. In this case, the majority of the electrons from the emitter are able to penetrate through the base region into the n-type material of the collector. Now, the base–collector junction has been reverse biased, and so any electrons injected into the collector region are rapidly removed through it to the positive supply terminal to which it is connected.

One way in which this doping can be carried out in manufacture

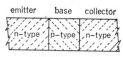

Figure 1.2

is by commencing with a lightly doped, p-type wafer and attaching to each side of it a suitable n-type impurity. Subsequent controlled heating causes alloying with the semiconductor, so setting up the n-type regions which form the emitter and the collector. This mechanism, known as overdoping, produces the relatively impure regions of low resistivity which are required, still leaving a very thin base region between them of high-resistivity, p-type material. A transistor made in this way is an alloy junction transistor. A typical alloy junction transistor is illustrated in plate 1. By comparison with more recent devices such transistors may seem very crude.

When the base–emitter junction of a transistor is forward biased, a substantial current can be made to flow in the collector circuit, which is only a little less than the emitter current. Also, the base current is very small and is equal to the difference between the emitter and collector currents. The junction transistor can be regarded as a device which is capable of diverting the base–emitter electron current into the collector region, so long as the base–emitter junction is biased into conduction. When it is reverse biased, only a very small input current flows, so that there are no electrons available to the collector. Thus, when carriers are put into motion across the low-impedance base–emitter junction, they are injected into the high-impedance collector region. Since these currents in the emitter and collector regions are nearly of equal magnitude, this process is clearly capable of producing a voltage amplification at the collector, or output, so long as the base–emitter input is not reverse biased. Figure 1.3 shows one way in which this may be brought about.

The figure shows a simple transistor amplifier with the input alternating signal applied to the base. In series with the signal is a bias voltage, E_b, so that the base–emitter junction is forward biased

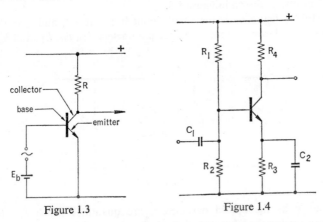

Figure 1.3   Figure 1.4

into conduction. The signal current then modifies the extent of this bias, and so the collector current varies with these changes. The collector current develops a potential across R, which thus is similar in shape to, and an amplified version of the input waveform.

Unfortunately, the intrinsic current, which also flows in the transistor, and so in the components associated with it, is liable to rise rapidly with temperature. This was particularly troublesome with the older, germanium transistors, but it must also be taken into account with the newer, silicon transistors. One way in which this problem can be counteracted is shown in figure 1.4.

The resistors R_1, R_2 and R_3 are used to combat two undesirable effects while providing the forward bias, E_b, already described. The first effect is the increase in intrinsic current as temperature rises. This doubles for every 8°C rise in temperature. The second is the reduction in forward bias, which is necessary to give a certain emitter current, which takes place as temperature rises. These components form a thermal, negative feedback loop, tending to make the collector current less dependent on temperature.

The performance of amplifiers of this kind is best examined with the aid of models or equivalent circuits. One of the better known of these replaces the transistor by two active elements and two passive elements, as shown in figure 1.5.

In the figure, i_b is the small, input base current, and i_c is the larger, collector current. The four parameters, h_{ie}, h_{re}, h_{fe}, and h_{oe},

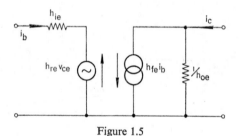

Figure 1.5

known as the hybrid parameters, are quantities which can be measured in the laboratory and which, when used in this equivalent circuit, enable essential data for any associated circuitry to be calculated.

A detailed discussion of hybrid parameters is out of place here, and the reader is referred to standard texts on this topic, one of which is to be found in the bibliography. However, it may be said that h_{ie} is the input impedance of the transistor when the output is short circuited. This is frequently of the order of a few thousand ohms. Thus, one of the drawbacks of simple transistor amplifiers is their low input impedance. The reason for this is that the input current is flowing in a forward-biased junction.

The current gain of the transistor, under similar conditions, is h_{fe}. This may, in practice, lie between about 5 and 1000, although it is typically within the range 50 to 200. If the load resistance is low, the current gain of the amplifier may often be almost as great as that of the transistor itself. In addition, h_{re} is the voltage feedback factor, and h_{oe} is the output conductance. Now, h_{oe} is relatively low, so that the output impedance of the transistor is high. This might have been expected, since the output impurity current is flowing in a reverse-biased junction.

p–n–p Transistors

If the reader examines figure 1.2 afresh, he will see that it represents a monocrystalline structure consisting of three layers. From the order of these layers, it is often said to represent an n–p–n transistor,

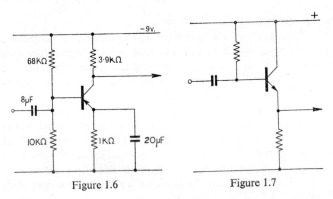

Figure 1.6   Figure 1.7

and the argument to this point has referred solely to this type of transistor. However, it is possible to use an alternative p–n–p structure. This uses an impure p-type emitter injecting holes across a relatively pure n-type base, into a p-type collector. In order to provide the correct bias to the junctions, different polarities are needed. The symbol for the transistor is changed also. (The arrow shows the direction of conventional current flow.) A typical amplifier is shown in figure 1.6. This uses a p–n–p transistor.

Emitter followers

We have seen that one of the problems of amplifier design is the low input impedance. Borrowing, no doubt, from the design of earlier valve amplifiers, it was soon found that increased input impedance could be achieved with the circuit of figure 1.7. Here also, the performance of the circuit can be analysed using the hybrid-parameter equivalent circuit of figure 1.5.

A circuit of the kind shown here could increase the input impedance by one or at most two orders, and two such circuits, operating in tandem, could do even better. Unfortunately, this kind of circuit, while having a high current gain, is not capable of a high voltage gain.

In a later chapter, we shall consider circuits capable of even higher input impedance.

Passive elements

The introduction of the transistor has a number of immediate effects on the design of electronic circuits. It was much smaller than the thermionic valve it replaced, and, in general, it tended to operate with less dissipation of power in the associated components. Working voltages were lower also. Thus the physical size of resistors was reduced, due in part to the lower dissipation, and in part to new manufacturing techniques. The use of tantalum electrolytic capacitors made it possible to place a high-capacity component (and high capacitance was required) in a very small space. Perhaps most important of all, the transistor readily lent itself to the use of printed circuits. These were made by etching the metal on a copper-clad, plastic board to a predetermined pattern, to replace the use of conventional wiring techniques.

Still, the passive components represented the greatest percentage of the space taken up by the circuit. Also, the greatest hindrances to the reliability of the circuit were the soldered connections to these components. Two solutions to this problem are of particular interest. These are *thin-film* circuits and semiconductor elements, in which the complete circuit is carried on a silicon slice. In addition, there are hybrid versions of these which must also be considered, these last being intended to combine some of the advantages claimed by the advocates of the other two methods.

CHAPTER 2

Thin-Film Integrated Circuits

In the effort to produce a highly reliable circuit, one possible technique which has been mentioned is that of depositing circuit elements onto some stable substrate. Typical substrates are borosilicate glass and ceramics such as glazed alumina. The purpose of the substrate is to support the film components it carries. Thus it must be flat and smooth. It must also be chemically inert, so that it does not react with the film deposited on it, or deteriorate during manufacture. In use, the substrate is first carefully cleaned, an ultrasonic bath being commonly used for this. After rinsing in high-purity water, the substrates are stored in a clean air room, at slightly above atmospheric pressure, to prevent them becoming contaminated by dust.

Deposition methods
There are a number of ways in which the circuit elements may be placed on the substrate. One of the most common is vacuum deposition at a pressure better than 10^{-4} torr. This method is used for resistance materials, such as chromium and nichrome. In this process, precision art work is used to prepare an etched mask in stainless steel. At low pressure, the metal to be deposited is electrically heated in a crucible or hung on a tungsten wire. When the wire is heated, surface tension causes the liquid metal to run along the wire. In either case, as the heating continues, a metal vapour is formed, providing the pressure is sufficiently low. This vapour is then deposited through the mask onto the substrate.

An alternative method of heating uses an electron gun. This enables the heated area to be accurately defined. Further, it has the advantage that a high degree of cleanliness is more easily obtained.

Vacuum deposition is also used for laying down a pattern of high-conductivity metal to act as the interconnecting pattern of conductors for the electronic circuit.

Vapour plating is also used, in which some metals, but principally metal oxides, can be produced at relatively low temperatures by chemical decomposition.

Another important method is sputtering. This has the advantage of being carried out at room temperature. Some workers claim that sputtering produces a more uniform film than other methods. In this process, a potential difference of the order of several kilovolts is applied between an anode and a cathode of the desired material in the presence of an inert gas at low pressure. The gas is ionised, due to the high p.d., and the heavy, positive, gas ions which are produced, bombard the cathode and release ions of the cathode material which are then deposited on the substrate. Tantalum is one resistance material which has been successfully deposited in this way.

Silk screening has also been used for thin-film circuits. This is a method using the direct application of suitable materials onto the substrate through a silk mask which is permeable over selected regions of its face. This is a technique which has been in use for a long time, for such applications as the printing of the tuning panels of radio receivers on glass. It is used, in the context of thin-film technology, for cermets and for some dielectric materials. Silk screening is usually limited to those cases where circuit tolerances are not very close and where the surface area of the substrate is large.

Finally, some mention should be made of chemical resists. The method used is similar to that employed in the manufacture of printed circuits, where a resist is coated on the substrate (in that case a copper-plastic laminate) and selectively hardened by the action of ultra-violet light. Subsequently, the soft resist is removed, so that the unprotected parts of the substrate may then be etched. This method is used where very close tolerance is required for the correct register of other components. Its advantages are that the masks are prepared on photographic film base, the costs of metal masks being avoided. However, the limit of line resolution is probably about 0·015 inch for commercial circuits.

Resistors

In one industrial process, the ceramic is first coated with a resist through a silk screen and then immersed in a palladium 'seeding'

Plate 1. *A photomicrograph of a low power p–n–p transistor. The pellet of p-type impurity in the centre shows the emitter lead from it. Mean diameter of transistor is 0·8 mm.*

Plate 2. *A planar n–p–n transistor (2N706). Note the ball-bonded gold wires to the emitter region, E, and to the base, B. The chip is about 0·5 mm square.*

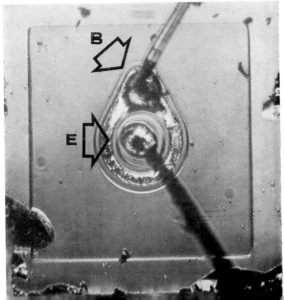

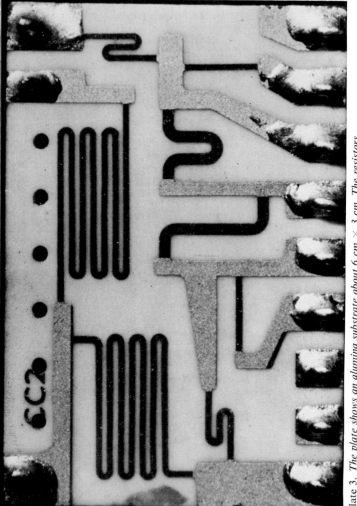

Plate 3. The plate shows an alumina substrate about 6 cm × 3 cm. The resistors and connectors have been formed by chemical deposition of nickel. Conventional soldering techniques have been used to make connections to the substrate.

Plate 4. *A multi-chip logic module. Isolation of the component chips is achieved by the four lands on the header. Note also the 0·5 mm square transistor chip, S, and the leads connected to the header, H, and to a terminal post, 1.*

Plate 5. *An array of three MOS devices on a single chip. Note the single diffusion area and the insulated region on which the gates have been deposited. There are four apertures in the insulation for the source and drain connections. The overall size of the array is 0·8 mm square.*

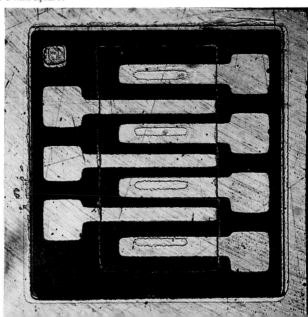

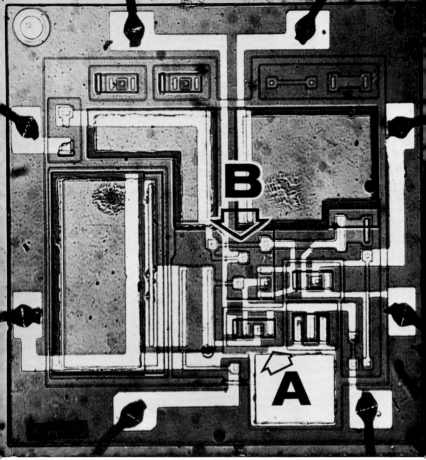

Plate 6. *A 1·5 mm square chip with a high gain amplifier whose frequency response extends to 100 Mc/s. Note the transistor, A, and the resistor, B. Observe particularly the transistor on the same land as this resistor. Its base is directly coupled to the collector of the transistor on its right and to the resistor, B.*

bath, so that when it is subsequently transferred to a nickel bath deposition of nickel takes place. The temperature of the second bath, and the immersion time in it enable the surface resistivity to be adequately controlled. Subsequent removal of the resist ink in an ultrasonic cleaning bath leaves the pattern of the resistors. The thin-film circuit illustrated in plate 3 has been produced in this way on an alumina substrate. The circuit carries eight resistors and the variations in *length-to-width ratio* can be clearly seen. The active elements and capacitors are on the other side of the substrate, which has been plated through at a number of points.

A typical, minimum thickness for a vacuum-deposited resistor is 100 Ångströms.* This helps to ensure that the resistor will be free from defects due to the irregular deposition of material. It is usual to quote the surface resistivity† of a deposit in ohms per square. For example, the surface resistivity of nichrome is about 125 ohms per square for a deposit 150 Ångströms thick. With this, it is possible to achieve an absolute accuracy of ± 10 per cent. In the processes which have been described, it is easier to hold the accuracy of one resistor relative to another than to keep the absolute accuracy low. Thus, it is usual to quote a proportional accuracy of ± 5 per cent. as a typical figure. By changing the thickness of the film and the substance used, it is possible to deposit films with resistivity up to at least 250 kilohms per square. The resistance of the element will be determined in part by the geometry of the mask. The dissipation which must be achieved will also influence the mask shape. Thus, if the surface resistivity is p, and the resistance required is R, it is possible to relate the length, l, of the film and its width, w, as follows.

$$R = pl/w \qquad (2.1)$$

Then the length-to-width ratio, l/w, can be found, so that, for instance, for a 300 ohms per square deposit, a 3 kilohm resistor can be produced if a length-to-width ratio of 10 is used. Now, if a constant voltage, V, be applied across the component, it can easily be seen that the power dissipated, W, is given by equation (2.2).

* 1 Ångström $= 10^{-8}$ centimetres.
† This is sometimes known as the sheet resistance.

$$W = \frac{V^2 w}{pl} \qquad (2.2)$$

Hence, the width of the film is determined by the power which must be dissipated, and the length-to-width ratio by the actual resistance required.

If the maximum dissipation per square inch which can be permitted is W_{max}, then,

$$W = W_{max} lw$$

and substituting for w from equation (2.1), we have

$$W = \frac{W_{max} l^2 p}{R}$$

or $$l = \sqrt{\left(\frac{WR}{W_{max} p} \right)} \qquad (2.3)$$

Hence, if the constant W_{max} for the material is known, the dimensions of the resistor can be found from W, R, and p.

It is not unusual to dissipate up to about 1 watt per square inch of resistor material. Provided the power dissipated is small, the resistor width may be as low as 0·01 inch.

Cermets are a common group of resistor materials. These may be metal–ceramic compounds, such as chromium silicon oxide; or, in an alternative form, a suspension of glass and platinum black with other powdered metals, similar in consistency to aquadag, is fired so that a cermet is produced. This material can be applied to the substrate by silk screening.

Temperature coefficient of resistance of thin films

The temperature coefficient of resistance is typically 3×10^{-5} per °C. Whilst this is still positive, it is lower than that of the bulk material. The temperature coefficient is dependent on the film thickness. It is not easy to maintain the coefficient at or near zero over a wide range of temperature. However, it is desirable that the resistance of the thin-film resistor varies in a reproducible way when it is repeatedly cycled over a given temperature range. If this is not so, this may be due to the introduction of strains between the metal and the substrate or to oxidation of the metal.

Voltage coefficient of resistance

The resistance of a thin film depends on the voltage applied across it. The voltage coefficient of resistance, β, is defined by the relationship

$$\beta = \frac{1}{R}\frac{dR}{dV}$$

where R is the resistance at a voltage V. A typical value of β is 1×10^{-6} per volt.

Interconnections

Connections to a resistance element can be made using a second mask through which aluminium, copper, or gold is evaporated onto the substrate. Part of the success of thin-film circuits is due to the toughness of the molecular bond which can be made between the substrate and the metal conductors. A typical surface resistivity for connecting materials is of the order of 0·02 ohms per square, with a typical thickness of 10^{-5} inch.

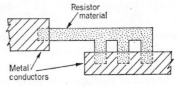

Figure 2.1

When resistors are produced by electrodeposition, as already described, it is possible to print a second mask on the pattern of nickel resistors, and so deposit a much thicker layer of nickel on those parts of the circuit which are to become connectors. This material can, of course, be soldered after removal of the resist, without other treatment. This has been done with the circuit shown in plate 2.

By using suitable masks, it is possible to adjust the ohmic value of resistors after the connecting conductors have been laid down. A practical method is shown in figure 2.1, where a resistor is shown which can be adjusted to have one of three values by scraping away the conductor from between the limbs of the resistor, at the right of the figure.

With this method, changes in resistance can only be made in a limited number of fixed steps. However, if the surface of the resistor is abrased, it can be adjusted by thinning the deposit. This is not usually possible with an evaporated resistor, but with silk-screened resistors or those produced by electrodeposition it is quite easy.

An alternative method for adjustment after fabrication is available when tantalum has been used as a resistance material. Here, it is possible to produce tantalum oxide by thermal treatment. Partial oxidation by carefully controlled heating gives a close control of the resistance of tantalum resistors. This method is particularly suitable where all the resistive elements on a substrate may be adjusted together.

Capacitors

Capacitors are formed from layers of conductor, between which a dielectric layer has been deposited. The capacitance, C, of a parallel plate capacitor is approximately given by equation (2.4).

$$C = \frac{kaN}{11 \cdot 31 d} \text{pF} \tag{2.4}$$

where k is the permittivity. A typical dielectric is silicon monoxide, with $k = 4$. This is evaporated onto the substrate. Alternatively, aluminium silicate has been employed, using a gas plating method. The area of overlap of the plates is a in equation (2.4), and N is the number of dielectrics. This is numerically one less than the number of plates. Also, d is the distance between plates, that is the dielectric thickness. A typical value depends on the breakdown voltage required; for example, $d = 10^4$ Ångströms for 50 volts working. The layer of metal produced by evaporation would be built up at about 50 Ångströms per second. Clearly, from equation (2.4), to produce a high capacitance, d should be made as small as possible. Typical surface capacities are from 0·04 to 0·4 microfarad per square inch. When capacitors are formed on ceramic, it is important that the ceramic be glazed first, or irregularities in its surface could produce regions where the electric field gradient was sufficient to cause breakdown.

One anodising technique is to deposit one electrode and then anodise it to allow partial oxidation to take place, but stopping the oxidation before all the metal has been attacked, so keeping one metal electrode. The second electrode is then deposited on the anodised metal. The periphery of the first layer should not have any sharp edges, so that, subsequently, voltage breakdown there is not encouraged.

Sputtering of metal surfaces is usually slower than evaporation (about 1 Ångström per second) and for oxides is less than this.

An alternative technique produces a dielectric by anodising tantalum, which has previously been deposited by sputtering. Somewhat thinner dielectrics can be tolerated here for a given working voltage, and hence larger surface capacities are available (typically, 1·0 microfarad per square inch).

One of the problems in making capacitors is to ensure that the dielectric has adequate strength, with low electrical conductivity, and at the same time to ensure that the dielectric is not subject to stress. Films which are in tensile stress are liable to fracture, but films in compressive stress are more acceptable. Zinc sulphide and silicon monoxide are frequently used as dielectrics.

Silicon monoxide can be evaporated at about 1 Ångström per second, and yields a corresponding permittivity of about 3·5. Evaporation must take place under strict conditions of cleanliness, since the presence of dust on the substrate can result later in breakdown of the dielectric when a field is applied across it. This problem may be avoided by care, or by depositing a layer of silicon on the oxide so that the layer is strengthened, the silicon being partially oxidised in the process. Finally, annealing at about 375°C can be used to give a worthwhile reduction in power factor.

Inductors

The design of thin-film circuits which involve inductors is not at all easy. Attempts have been made to use transistor circuits to simulate the voltage–current phase relationship typical of inductors, but with only slight success. Here, however, we are concerned with the production of inductors, whose properties depend on shaping conductors into the form of a coil. This is more easily effected by thin-film methods than by other techniques. However, the small size of the substrate limits the maximum inductance to low values (less than 1 microhenry), despite any effort to use a large number of turns. Also, the thinness of the metal film increases its resistance, and so lowers its Q.

One point to be borne in mind is that the presence of an inductor may introduce magnetic and electrostatic coupling with nearby circuit elements. Stray fields can be reduced by shielding the coil with a ferromagnetic material, so increasing the inductance at the same time, although perhaps adding resistive losses also. In addition to the usual problem of reduced frequency response, there are the difficulties of manufacturing suitable shielding materials in thin-film form. One method which has been used employs two layers of ferrite to form a shield. This is often put in place by hand, because attempts to enclose the coil totally in ferrite, by evaporation techniques, involve temperatures at which the coil would be destroyed.

Active components

One of the problems of thin-film circuits is the difficulty of producing diodes and transistors by similar techniques to those just described for passive components and by the deposition of cadmium sulphide and selenide. While this has been done in the laboratory, large-scale production is not yet available. Hence, manufacturers have to concentrate on using transistors which are physically very small, of the order of 1 millimetre thick, which can be connected directly to the evaporated conductors.

Thus, whilst the early, thin-film circuits used conventional transistors (often in TO 18 cans), resin-encapsulated transistors were used later. The development of flip chip transistors has since made it possible to avoid the necessity for separate encapsulation of the transistors. These are small, silicon chips, each of which carries a transistor. By suitable surface masking treatment, they can be bonded directly to the thin-film metal conductors.

Connecting leads

Leads from the substrate, and from the transistors and diodes to the conductors can be attached by electric welding or thermocompression bonding. An alternative method is to use soldering, but to avoid possible damage by conventional soldering a non-contact method is sometimes used. The soldering-iron consists of a single turn of fine copper tubing, through which hydrogen gas is directed onto the substrate. The gas is heated by passing a current along the coil, so heating it, and, since hydrogen has a high thermal conductivity, heating the gas also. Thus, not only is the hot gas directed on a very small piece of solder in the working area, but also the soldering is done in the atmosphere of the gas rather than in the oxidising atmosphere of the air.

Finally, the substrate can be stacked with another substrate above the circuit, where dissipation levels permit, to form a sandwich, or placed in some suitable plastic case, and encapsulated in some suitable material such as silicone rubber or epoxy resin.

Design principles

Thin-film techniques are particularly useful when a circuit has to be produced where the ratio of active to passive elements is low. A typical example is the circuit shown in figure 2.2.

This circuit respresents a transistor logic gate, which will be discussed in a later chapter from the point of view of the function it performs. Here, there are six passive elements (there may, in practice, be more) with one active element. It is, therefore, very suitable for using the thin-film technique.* In this case, one of the circuit parameters, which it is important to control, is the ratio of each of the identical input resistors to the common base resistor. Again, this is well suited to this method of construction, since the designer

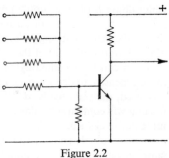

Figure 2.2

should aim to control resistance ratios rather than absolute values.

When designing a thin-film integrated circuit, the circuit is built first using conventional components, a worst case design method being used, since later design changes can be very expensive. However, the cost of setting up a plant for a run of some particular circuit is very much less than for the solid chip techniques, to be discussed in the next chapter. Thus, one of the important advantages

* A commercial example of this is the Elliott Minilog type F.1.

of thin-film circuits is where there is a requirement for short runs of a wide variety of circuits.

When a suitable design has been developed, it is possible to convert this to a thin-film design. It is outside the scope of this book to describe this in detail, but it should be pointed out that this design procedure is adopted to minimise the development costs which would otherwise arise. Production costs are primarily dependent on the number of circuit varieties, rather than on the total number of circuits required. Hence, care should be taken to see that as few different circuits as possible are used. Examples will illustrate this point in later chapters.

Resistor values should lie between 1 kilohm and 50 kilohms or as near to this range as possible, and the circuit should be designed for minimal power dissipation. For this reason, it is wise to operate at as low a voltage as possible; although, to avoid noise interference on the supply lines affecting the performance of high-gain amplifiers or logic elements, the supply voltage should be high. A reasonable compromise is often a supply potential of the order of 15 volts.

One of the problems of all microminiature circuit techniques is that of the manufacturing yield. If the microelectronic unit has large dimensions (in this case, if the substrate is large), then many circuit elements can be accommodated on it. Also, it is only marginally more expensive to deposit over a larger area. However, as the size is increased, the yield tends to fall, since it becomes more likely that the unit will contain some flaw. Also, a larger unit probably contains more active elements and, therefore, the cost will rise above that of a smaller unit. It should, though, be cheaper than the same circuitry accommodated on a number of smaller substrates. Thus, one limit to the size of the unit will be its replacement cost.

Yield problems are not very acute with thin-film circuits, and so the substrate area does, in fact, tend to become large. This has the effect of decreasing the number of interconnections between substrates in any given system. It is these connections which are most unreliable.

CHAPTER 3

Diffusion Techniques in Silicon

The germanium transistors described in chapter 1 were characterised by relatively high, intrinsic (leakage) currents, and by their ability to function as amplifiers only up to frequencies of a few megacycles per second. Also, they were much affected by changes in temperature, since, with the intrinsic current doubling for every 8°C rise, it was quite likely that, if a small impurity current was used, the leakage current would become greater than this impurity current at even moderate temperatures. Also, the transistor could be permanently damaged if the junction temperature were permitted to exceed about 90°C.

These problems were tackled first by using silicon instead of germanium as the basic semiconductor material. Until about 1954, it was not possible to produce silicon of sufficient purity for transistor manufacture. This level of purity was only obtained after zone refining a large number of times. Leakage currents were much smaller, and the maximum operating temperature was raised to about 150°C. However, the main reasons for the poor performance, even of silicon transistors, at high frequencies were the capacitances which were associated with the junctions. There was a large input capacitance and, more important, a capacitive connection between the input and the output. These are effects which are not explained using the simple model of figure 1.5. These capacitances prevented any worthwhile amplification at high frequencies.

There have been a number of technological developments, which have resulted in transistors being produced which were capable of operating at progressively higher frequencies. Some of these are not relevant here, for they appear to have no important place in microelectronics.

Now, the purpose of discussing the development of transistors and the construction of thin-film and semiconductor microcircuits is to enable the reader to compare the various commercial products and to assess which of them are best suited to any applications with which he is involved. For this reason, the development from the alloy transistor to more sophisticated devices will not be considered in detail. Instead, only a few transistor types, appropriate to the subject of this book, will be considered here.

Planar double-diffused transistors

Figure 3.1 shows the structure of a planar, diffused transistor. The n-type material of the silicon slice, which will later form the collector, is coated with an oxide layer; this is laid down using a precision mask, in much the same way as in the production of thin-film circuits, except that here the geometrical shapes involved are very much smaller. This oxide layer then itself acts as a mask, preventing diffusion from taking place at those parts of the surface of the semiconductor slice where it has been applied. A p-type impurity is used for diffusion, the dopant being conveyed by a carrier gas,

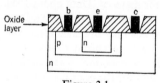

Figure 3.1

boron being frequently used, at a temperature of about 1200°C. Diffusion of this impurity into the silicon slice takes place, where it is unprotected, to form the base of the transistor. It is important to note that the diffused p-type region has the same crystal orientation

as the original n-type material, just as in the alloy transistor, the same crystal lattice was maintained throughout the transistor. After remasking, a second diffusion of n-type material, often phosphorus, is carried out to form the emitter. Finally, contacts are made to the layers through openings in the oxide layer. These contacts are formed by evaporating a thin layer of metal over the whole of the oxide surface, and then removing the unwanted parts by photoresist techniques. At present, aluminium is used for this purpose, as it makes good ohmic contacts with both p-type and n-type silicon. However, if gold wires are to be attached to these contacts, a reaction may take place between the two metals at high temperatures; this results in a high-resistance contact which causes corrosion of the aluminium. This is sometimes known as *purple plague*. It is one of a number of intermetallic compounds, probably $AuAl_2$, which have the property of dissolving silicon. It is a good conductor with a resistivity of about that of nickel. The name arises from its purple colour; while in the presence of silicon it is almost black.* Gold wire has been used for contacts to silicon integrated circuits, because it is relatively chemically inert and is very malleable. Thus, it is easy to use thermocompression bonding for making contact to the aluminium. Unfortunately, silicon acts as a catalyst for the formation of purple plague. Probably the best solution to this problem, at the moment, is to use aluminium wire, thus avoiding purple plague at the semiconductor chip, although it can still occur, but more slowly, at the gold-plated post of the can or flat pack in which the chip is held. In the absence of silicon, a much higher activation energy is required, so that in practice a long life for the device may be expected.

Planar, diffused transistors are capable of operation at much higher frequencies than the older, alloy types and, partly due to the oxide layer, are very stable, and have an intrinsic current of the order of tens of nanoamps. However, the typical impurity density which is required for successive diffusions results in the collector layer being relatively pure (about 10^{17} atoms per cubic centimetre), so that subsequent layers could be successively more impure. Thus the collector layer has a high resistivity. This is not particularly suitable for those applications where the collector carries a large current, or where the potential difference between collector and emitter must be made to fall almost to zero. This means that the collector can be considered as having a substantial series resistance. This defect is overcome in the planar, epitaxial transistor.

Planar epitaxial transistors

In the epitaxial transistor, a heavily doped layer, marked n+ in figure 3.2, is used as the collector. Because of its low resistivity, some of the drawbacks of double-diffused transistors are overcome. A thin, epitaxial, n-type layer, which is lightly doped, is then grown

* Sometimes known as 'black death'.

on this layer, and the transistor is formed by diffusion in the layer in the same way as before. In epitaxial transistors, the heavily doped substrate has a much larger volume than that of the epitaxial layer upon it, in which the transistor is formed.

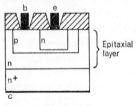

Figure 3.2

A typical planar transistor is illustrated in plate 2. Note the ball-bonded gold leads to the base and emitter. The area of the complete slice is about one-tenth of that of the alloy junction transistor illustrated in plate 1.

Planar diodes

The construction of diodes can follow similar lines to that of transistors, diffused and epitaxial types being available. However, in pursuing the purpose of this book, we shall be discussing the use of diodes in integrated circuits, on the same semiconductor chip as transistors. Because of this, it is convenient to produce only transistors on the substrate, and when the connections are subsequently laid down, some of the transistors can then be connected to act as

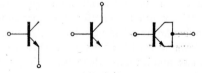

Figure 3.3

diodes. This has the advantage that a number of different connections are possible, three of which are shown in figure 3.3, thus influencing the performance of the diodes which are made in this way.

The characteristics of diodes are determined by the doping of the layers and by the junction area. The first of these factors is dependent on the design of the associated transistors. Thus the designer has still some control over the diodes which are finally used, by selecting the connections he will use.

Figure 3.3a shows the capacitances associated with a diode; namely, its shunt capacitance, C_S, and the capacitances, C_A and C_B, to the epitaxial layer. If a base-collector junction diode is used, it will have low capacitances, and its reverse recovery time* will be very short. This type of diode is therefore most suited for a low-charge storage diode. If the base-emitter junction is used, longer storage times result as shown in table 3.1.

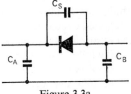

Figure 3.3a

Table 3.1 *Typical capacitances of diodes*

	C_A (pF)	C_B (pF)	C_S (pF)	Reverse recovery time
base–collector junction	2	0·3	0·2	Short
base–emitter junction	1	1·5	1·0	Medium
base–emitter junction with base shorted to collector	1	1·0	1·0	Long

Silicon integrated circuits

We have seen that the reduction in volume occupied by an electronic circuit, occasioned by the introduction of the transistor, was ultimately responsible for the development of thin-film techniques, on the grounds of increased reliability, thus reducing the volume yet further. In the same way, the alloy transistor was only a step in the evolution of solid state technology. The silicon double-diffused transistor and the planar epitaxial transistor were further stages of development which were capable of use at higher frequencies. These gave research workers and manufacturers considerable experience of evaporation and diffusion in monocrystalline semiconductors. It should not be thought that, because these new skills have been quickly dismissed here, they were without their rewards. By 1967 a great part, probably the major part, of the electronics industry was directly benefiting from the knowledge gained and was using diffused and epitaxial transistors in preference to the older types.

* For definition and further discussion of reverse recovery see: Dean, K. J., 'Transistors: Theory and Circuitry', McGraw-Hill (1964), p. 141 et seq.

However, the author believes that history will judge these transistors to be only further stages in the development of highly reliable circuits. Industry has already demonstrated that this reliability can be obtained either by the thin-film method or by silicon integrated circuitry. Attention has been focused on measurements of the mean time between failures of these circuits. Already people are talking of 'second generation' integrated circuits, as more experience is gained in this work.

The first step towards integration is to fabricate a number of transistors on the same silicon slice. In itself, this is a useful step, because there are a number of applications in which the performance of a group of transistor amplifiers must be closely matched. This matching is made easier when the transistors have very closely

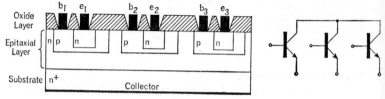

Figure 3.4

controlled, similar dimensions, and are formed at the same time, alongside each other on the same slice of semiconductor. In particular, temperature conditions are likely to be almost identical.

A typical multiple transistor is shown in figure 3.4. The additional cost of producing three transistors instead of one will be somewhat greater than before, because the yield of elements having no defects may be smaller than it was previously. However, it should not be as much as for three, entirely separate transistors. Generally, the more complex the masking pattern, the lower the yield tends to be, and consequently the more comprehensive the test programme which must be carried out by the manufacturer. One disadvantage of the particular arrangement shown in figure 3.4 is that the collectors of the transistors are formed in the common epitaxial layer, and are thus in good electrical contact. Figure 3.5 shows one way in which this can be overcome.

The figure shows two n–p–n transistors formed by triple diffusion into a p-type substrate. This is a process which is clearly an extension of double diffusion, and is used by the manufacturers of individual transistors. Here it will be seen from the figure that the substrate is not used for the collector layer. In this example, the n-type collectors make p–n junctions with the substrate, and, provided these junctions are reverse biased, each transistor is isolated though the relatively high, capacitive impedance of the p–n diode. The correct bias conditions can be brought about if the substrate is held negative with respect to the collectors. One of the problems of diffused junctions is that high reverse voltages, in excess of about 40 volts, lead to a breakdown of the junction. It is necessary to consider

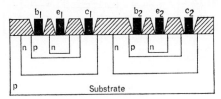

Figure 3.5

high voltages because the reverse-biased junction acts as a capacitor, and its capacitance, C, depends on the magnitude of the reverse voltage, V, where C is proportional to $V^{-1/3}$. This high voltages are desirable if the capacitances between collectors of different transistors are to be kept small. One of the most pressing design problems in silicon integrated circuitry is this capacitive coupling, through the substrate, between individual elements on it.

A further problem is that the substrate acts as the collector of a parasitic p–n–p transistor. This is formed with the collector and base of each of the useful transistors acting as base and emitter respectively of the *parasite*.* One of the effects of parasitic transistors on the performance of amplifiers and switches is to act as a capacitive load, so reducing the gain of the amplifier or the speed of the switch. Now it is possible to control the geometry of the device

* This is sometimes known as 'parasitic plague'.

so that the current gain of the parasite is of the order of 2 to 5. This is brought about by using rather deep collector diffusion because the collector, acting as the base of the parasite, can then be made to have a low transport factor.*

The drawbacks of double-diffused transistors, which were mentioned earlier, are also true of these devices. Just as they were overcome by the use of epitaxy, so they can be similarly dealt with here.

Figure 3.6 shows a part of a silicon slice to which an epitaxial

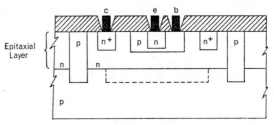

Figure 3.6

layer has been applied. An n–p–n transistor has then been formed in this epitaxial layer. Diffusion of a p-type impurity has been used to isolate the transistor from adjoining devices, and an n^+ diffusion has been used to lower the series collector impedance. However, silicon integrated circuits have not responded as effectively as individual transistors to this technique. A further n^+-type buried layer, shown dotted in the figure, has been used by some manufacturers to improve the performance of integrated epitaxial transistors. For some time, however, the performance of silicon integrated transistors was poorer than that of corresponding conventional types. This was partly due to the capacitance of the reverse-biased diode formed by the collector and the substrate, shunting the collector circuit. In addition, the collector saturation resistance is seldom less than 20 ohms, thus impairing its performance as a switch.

* Transport factor can be defined as the ratio of the number of carriers which are able to cross from the base to the collector to the number which enter the base when it is biased into conduction.

This is because the collector connection is made to the upper surface of the silicon chip. Therefore, the collector current must pass through the relatively high-resistance epitaxial layer twice. Since this resistance is, therefore, larger than in a conventional, discrete transistor, the change in resistance due to temperature changes is also larger. These effects are sometimes countered by using two collector contacts. This reduces the collector saturation voltage also.

For these reasons, many earlier integrated amplifier circuits had poorer frequency response and longer switching times than discrete amplifiers.

One of the features of the design of transistors as parts of silicon integrated circuits is that it is possible for the designer to vary the geometry of the transistor to suit the particular circuit with which he is concerned. As already described, he is able to control the collector saturation voltage and the associated resistance. Similarly, variations in size and number of base contacts will modify the base saturation voltage and resistance, and the capacitance between the base and the substrate.*

For a transistor to be a good switch, the epitaxial layer should be as thin as possible, in order to keep stray capacitances low, and to achieve lower storage time. Also, the epitaxial layer is a relatively high resistivity layer, and if this is kept thin the transistors formed in it will have a lower saturation resistance, since the resistance between the buried collector layer and the active collector region will be less. This incidentally implies that the diffusion time cycles in manufacture will be less, since only a thinner layer is required.

When thin-film circuits were discussed in chapter 2, it was suggested that a good indication of the performance of the circuit could be made from a model in which conventional components were used. So far, the discussion of silicon integrated circuits has been concerned with diodes and transistors, but, as will be seen later, passive components can also be included in the silicon chip.

One of the advantages of silicon integrated circuits is that the stray capacitances with the can, which are present in a discrete transistor, are missing. Since it is now part of an integrated circuit,

* Any capacitance to the layer in which the circuit element is held is called a land capacitance, since this isolated layer is known as a land.

there will be no leads from the transistor to the terminal posts which pass through the seal. Similarly, wiring capacitances will be missing. However, owing to the parasitic transistors and capacitance of reverse-biased junctions, there is a great deal of interaction between elements in the circuit. Hence, it cannot be said that a conventional component model will give a good guide to the performance of the silicon integrated circuit. Many designers would estimate that although they are aware of this problem, it is at least equally likely that the layout of a new circuit will need modification as that it will be satisfactory in the form in which it was first designed. Although much can be done by taking layout into account in the first instance, other techniques for the effective isolation of circuit elements can be mentioned here also.

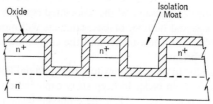

Figure 3.7

A satisfactory production method does not appear to have been found for growing monocrystalline silicon on a polycrystalline substrate, although laboratory experiments in this direction are encouraging. This has been one of the problems confronting the designer of thin-film circuits, with the result that the small, active elements, transistors and diodes, have usually to be connected to the thin film, since they cannot be produced on it in the same way as the passive elements. One possible way to isolate elements on a silicon chip, but for this drawback, would be the use of a polycrystalline substrate. What is practicable, however, is to grow a low-resistivity n^+ layer on a monocrystalline, n-type, silicon slice which has a higher resistivity than the layer. A suitable pattern is then etched through this n^+ layer into the n-type substrate beneath, to form 'isolation moats'. Afterwards, an oxide layer is diffused onto this, as shown in figure 3.7.

Above these moats, it is possible to deposit a thick epitaxial layer of polycrystalline silicon which later is used as the substrate. Subsequently, the n-type silicon is lapped to remove the material which is represented by the lower part of figure 3.7, below the dotted line.

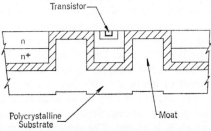

Figure 3.8

It is then possible to form the circuit elements in the remaining parts of the n-type layer as indicated in figure 3.8, in which the remaining part of figure 3.7 is inverted.

This technique can be used to make devices with a very much higher breakdown voltage between individual elements, in excess of 1 kilovolt, and, if the oxide layer is sufficiently thick, perhaps several microns, the capacitance between elements can be made very small.

Passive elements

When considering the development of thin-film circuits, it was pointed out that passive elements could be constructed with a large measure of control, whereas active elements could not be deposited as part of the thin film. For this reason, thin-film circuits are used where there is a high ratio of passive to active elements.

With integrated circuits, it is easy to produce active elements, transistors and diodes, but passive elements take up a relatively large part of the surface area of the chip. Hence, silicon integrated circuits are more useful than thin-film circuits where there is a lower ratio of passive to active elements. It is difficult to manufacture resistors to close tolerances, and the range of component values is more restricted than for thin-film techniques. For these reasons, active devices are always to be preferred in semiconductor integrated circuits to passive components. Thus, transistors and diodes can often be used to replace resistors, in, for example, the coupling between amplifier stages.

Resistors can be formed by diffusion of an n-type layer, for instance, on the p-type substrate, so that each resistor can be held at a potential which will keep the diode, of which it is a part, reverse biased and so isolated from other components. One common practice is to lay down resistors at the same time as the collectors of the transistors on the same slice. The surface resistivity of a typical collector layer might be 500 ohms per square, with a resistance temperature coefficient of about 2×10^{-3} per °C. With the voltages employed in many circuits, it may be difficult to ensure that the resistor material is always reverse biased, when compared with the substrate on which it is placed. The doping can be increased to assist this, or the resistor can be placed in a separately biased layer. Where very low resistance values are required, it is sometimes possible to use the very impure emitter diffusion (instead of collector diffusion), typically about 25 ohms per square. It is thus possible to produce resistors whose resistance lies in the range 100 ohms to 10 kilohms.

Resistors can be laid down at the same time as the base diffusion. A typical sheet resistance is then 100 ohms per square. Whatever layer is used, the width of a typical resistor is about 1/1000 inch, depending on the resistance value required. Very low and very high resistance values are expensive owing to the adverse geometrical construction and uneconomical use of chip area.

The temperature coefficient of these resistors passes through a minimum at about room temperature, then rising at about 9×10^{-4} per °C.

Pinch effect resistors

Resistors take up a considerable area on a silicon slice, particularly where high-resistance values are required. If it is assumed that a 2 kilohm resistor takes about the same area as a transistor, it will become obvious that, to avoid, for example, a 10 kilohm resistor in a circuit, it will be advantageous to employ up to four transistors. The circuit designer must, therefore, minimise the use of passive elements, and where resistors are necessary restrict their use to the range 10 ohms to 2 kilohms.

Occasionally, it is necessary to employ very high ohmic values, and pinch effect resistors are then used. The base diffusion is often used to produce these elements. The resistive channel in which current flows is surrounded by a reverse-biased junction, the potential on which restricts the channel by depletion, so giving a high resistance. Such resistors have the disadvantage of very wide resistance tolerance. They have been used for biasing transistors; where the spread of current gain and this tolerance tend, to some extent, to compensate each other in the production of a silicon chip.

Capacitors

Capacitors may be formed in two ways. In the first method a junction diode may be produced and operated in the reverse-biased mode. This is useful for a low capacitance, but the capacitor is voltage sensitive, and its capacitance also depends on the doping of the electrode layers. There is also the need to ensure that it is held in reverse bias, by suitable, direct potentials.

One of the limitations of all integrated circuits is the difficulty of producing high capacitances. One technique which has been used depends on siting a highly doped, p-type, diffused layer immediately between the buried n^+ layer (see figure 3.6) and a second n^+ region in the epitaxial layer. These layers form junctions which are effectively in parallel. Capacitors of greater than 2 picofarads per square thousandth of an inch have been achieved in this way.

An alternative method uses silicon monoxide layers, which are produced as part of the masking process. These are formed by heating the silicon slice in a furnace, in an atmosphere of steam. The intention is to use this oxide layer as a dielectric between conducting layers. The dielectric can be very thin, provided that a high working voltage is not required, but the maximum capacitance is limited to about 500 picofarads by the surface area of the plates, for it is clearly not possible to tolerate too large an area.*

* A more practicable maximum value is about 150 picofarads. Capacitances greater than about 50 picofarads can only be achieved with very thin dielectrics, so increasing the risk of pinholes and poor dielectric strength.

If a silicon monoxide layer is being used as a dielectric, then it is possible to evaporate a conducting layer on it, by the methods used with thin films, in the same way that connections are made both to thin films and to integrated circuits, so ensuring a high-conductivity 'plate' for the capacitor.

Zener diodes

Zener diodes are semiconductor devices across which a nearly constant voltage can be produced for a wide range of current through the diode. They have been made by using the breakdown voltage of a reverse-biased diode, but if a low dynamic impedance is required it is necessary to use a large junction area. Alternatively, it is possible to use a transistor for this, using the breakdown between collector and base. If connections are only made to the collector and emitter, the device acts as a zener diode coupled to an emitter follower.* Hence, a lower dynamic impedance can be obtained for a smaller surface area.

Hybrid circuits

The use of thin-film techniques in the manufacture of silicon integrated circuits can also be extended to the deposition of resistors. Hybrid† structures of this kind can often be used with advantage, although they are generally more expensive, since more processes are involved in their manufacture. They have the advantage of reducing the distributed capacitances associated with the element, and often eliminate undesirable parasitic transistors. Hybrid circuits, therefore, consist of silicon circuits produced by diffusion and epitaxy, on which a passivating layer has been applied, and on this the thin-film components have been laid down. In this way, it is possible to utilise the lower temperature coefficients of resistance, characteristic of thin-film resistors and the greater precision and closer tolerances with which they can be made. The need for reverse bias, to isolate passive components, is thus also eliminated, while the

* An emitter follower is a simple transistor circuit, one of the characteristics of which is its very low output impedance (see figure 1.7).

† The term 'hybrid' is applied to circuits which use both silicon chip and thin-film techniques. The term 'monolithic' has been applied to circuits which use only silicon chip methods.

surface resistivity of the resistor material is no longer linked to that of any of the diffused layers. The thin-film capacitors, already described, can also be constructed at the same time.

The term 'hybrid' has been used elsewhere to describe circuits in which separate silicon chips are assembled on a single ceramic substrate, which also carries a pattern of thin films. Sometimes, integrated silicon chips and thin-film circuits have been assembled on the same header, no attempt being made to mount them on a common substrate. In this case, the only electrical contacts are the welded gold wires, which connect the individual substrates to the header. Multi-chip circuits of this type are probably only a temporary expedient, just as a discrete resistor itself can now be regarded as a passing (though somewhat long) phase in the development of microelectronic circuits. It seems very probable, at the present time, that this development will, in future, use both thin-film and silicon chip techniques. Plate 4 shows a typical multi-chip circuit. Two of the chips each carry a single transistor, two carry resistor networks, and one carries diodes. The header has been separated into four gold-plated lands to isolate the chips.

It might be argued that a manufacturer who uses silicon integrated circuits on which a conducting pattern is evaporated could be said to be employing a hybrid technique. Here, however, the term will be reserved for those production methods in which the circuit elements themselves are not all produced by only one of the two fundamental processes.

Design of silicon integrated circuits

It is not intended here to consider in great detail the design problems of integrated circuits, for the same reasons that, in older books on electronics, the details of valve manufacture were often not considered. The systems designer, however, needs to know something of the problems facing the device and circuit designer, and, in particular, the limitations of the media with which they work.

The manufacturing processes can be summarised as follows. It is first necessary to grow an extremely pure silicon crystal, whose structure is monocrystalline. This is typically about 4 centimetres in diameter. It is later cut into slices which are lapped, polished, and etched, until clean, smooth surfaces are obtained. These surfaces are subsequently oxidised.

A photolithographic process is used to remove this oxide selectively in those parts of the slice where circuit elements will be deposited. The first diffusion, using a p-type slice, would be of phosphorus vapour. This leads to an impurity region of low resistivity known as the collector diffusion region. The oxide is then regrown and again selectively removed. The diffusion process, which takes place at high temperatures, is then repeated using a boron gas. The oxide coating is removed and a high-resistivity, n-type, epitaxial diffusion carried out. When this has been completed, the oxide layer can be re-formed. This is usually carried out using steam to oxidise the silicon surface.

The subsequent steps in the process are then identical to those employed in the manufacture of silicon planar transistors, except that both active and passive components are produced by multiple diffusions, in the way already described.

When it is necessary to minimise minority-carrier storage times, as in switching circuits, gold doping is used. This is done after the diffusion processes, by evaporating gold onto the reverse face of the slice. Subsequent heat treatment results in the rapid diffusion of the gold through the silicon.

It should not be assumed that one is underestimating the problems of maintaining the registers of masks to dimensional accuracies of the order of 10^{-5} centimetre over a period of some days, and with changing temperatures, but rather that the problems of manufacturing technology, great as they are, are not our prime concern.

The main considerations in designing a silicon integrated circuit are the area of the silicon chip and the yield which can be achieved. The physical design of the circuit on the chip can affect both of these.

Typical chip sizes in current manufacture are from 20 to 100 thousandths of an inch squares. A large number of these circuits are produced on a single slice, each chip being separated by isolation channels of about 0·5 to 2 thousandths of an inch width. For instance, it is easily possible to produce 400 chips, each 40×40 thousandths of an inch, on a single slice, while more complicated circuits may require batches of about 60 chips, each 100 × 100 thousandths of an inch.

Because yield is an inverse function of chip size, the tendency has been for manufacturers to keep chip size as small as possible, limited by the precision with which components could be placed on the chip. Fortunately, since the circuit elements are simultaneously produced, the probability of obtaining a good circuit is greater than the product of the separate probabilities for each element. Today, yields of integrated circuits are of the same order as for discrete transistors.

The designer will be limited, by system considerations, to using

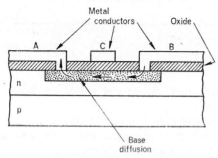

Figure 3.9

particular pins on the can for supply and input and output potentials. In making the circuit diagram satisfy these restraints, he must only use permitted cross-over connections, to avoid unwanted electrical contact.

One of the most common examples of a cross-over is shown in figure 3.9, where the base diffusion and oxide layers are employed to make contact between the metal conductors, A and B, without shorting to C. Somewhat less commonly, the buried n^+ layer can be used, as shown in figure 3.10, for the same purpose. There are other methods, using either an isolation diffusion or the emitter layer, but these are met less frequently.

The designer must decide on the number of lands he requires. The resistors will usually be on one land, which is connected perhaps

D

to the positive supply. This is only possible if no resistor is at a more positive potential than this. Similarly, all n–p–n transistors with common collector connections can be placed on a single land, or, if any collector is at the positive supply potential, on the resistor

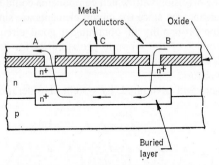

Figure 3.10

land. Care with these points will reduce the land capacitances already discussed.

These points have been mentioned to illustrate some of the compromises which must be effected, and to explain how it is that the final circuit, after design and fabrication, may have different parasitic capacitances than the discrete model from which it was designed. This is especially true for large-area resistors.

It is outside our present scope to discuss further the techniques of mask manufacture and the treatment of the silicon slice.

CHAPTER 4

Field Effect Transistors

Germanium alloy transistors have an input impedance* of the order of 2 kilohms; although the introduction of silicon epitaxial transistors brought many new advantages, they did little to improve this feature of semiconductor amplifiers. Considerable attention has been directed to circuit design in which a high input impedance is an essential feature. By such means, it is possible to raise impedances to the order of several megohms. Integrated circuits, however, impose certain limitations on the number and values of passive elements which can be accommodated on any given area of substrate. For this reason, it is often preferable, when using silicon chip (monolithic) circuits, to duplicate the functions of passive elements by active ones. This is particularly desirable where, for instance, resistor values are large or non-linear components are desirable. The field effect transistor is of particular value where circuits must have a high input impedance and where noise, generated by semiconductor active elements, is an important drawback of conventional, high-impedance circuits.

Field effect
The principle of operation of a field effect transistor can be illustrated with reference to figure 4.1, although this does not closely represent the most recent form of the device. The transistor is constructed from an n-type slab, two opposite ends of which are called the 'drain' and the 'source'. This n-type region is constricted between these ends by the presence of a p-type region called the 'gate', produced, perhaps, by diffusion. When a potential is applied between the drain and the source, the impurity current which flows passes through the constricted region, called the 'channel', so that there is a potential

* When used in the common emitter mode.

gradient along its length. If now, a potential is applied to the gate, so that the p–n junction between the gate and the channel is reverse biased, a depletion layer is formed near this junction. For this reason, this device is known as a depletion-type field effect transistor. Now, the width of this depletion layer is a function of the applied voltage, so that, as this voltage increases, the channel through which the impurity current flows becomes even more constricted. At some applied voltage, called the pinch-off voltage,* V_p, the depletion layer has become wide enough to reduce the slope conductance of the channel virtually to zero. Below the pinch-off voltage, the transistor acts as a voltage-controlled variable resistor. Between this voltage and some much higher voltage at which the usual avalanche effect

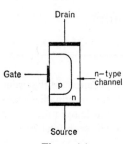

Drain

Gate

n–type channel

p

n

Source

Figure 4.1

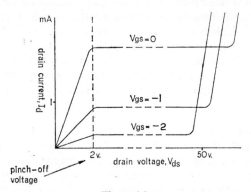

Figure 4.2

causes breakdown, the conductivity of the channel is so small that only a limited current is able to flow. This is called the saturated drain current. Typical characteristics are shown in figure 4.2.

* The name arises because at this voltage the drain current is pinched into a very thin sheet.

The current which flows in the channel consists, apart from the small intrinsic current, of electrons, since, in this example, an n-type channel was employed. These are the majority carriers and there is no injection, as in conventional transistors, of minority carriers from the input junction. The input junction, here, is always reverse biased, and no carriers have to move across a potential barrier. The presence of minority carriers and the movement of charges across potential barriers are effects which are responsible for the 'noise' in conventional transistors. Here, the absence of these effects results in high input impedance and low noise.

The name 'field effect* transistor' arises from the effect which the field due to the gate-source voltage, V_{gs}, has on the drain current. It is also called a unipolar transistor, because the carriers involved are almost all of one type or polarity – majority carriers.

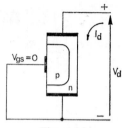

It should be noted that even when V_{gs} is zero, the pinch-off effect still occurs. This can be explained in terms of the potential drop along the length of the channel.

As shown in figure 4.3, the drain current flowing through the high-resistivity n-type channel makes the upper end of the chan-

Figure 4.3

nel, in the figure, positive with respect to the p-type gate. Thus, there is a reverse bias over part of the gate-source p–n junction, even though the gate and the source are connected. When the drain current is sufficiently high, this potential drop along the channel is thus able to cause pinch-off, as shown in figure 4.2. When the junction is externally reverse biased, only a smaller voltage is necessary, since the two effects are additive. Thus, in general terms, this pinch-off current is dependent on the gate-source bias voltage. This also is illustrated in figure 4.2.

The output resistance can be obtained from the slope of the characteristic in figure 4.2. The input impedance is that of the reverse-biased junction, and clearly it is desirable that this should be high. For this reason, and for reasons of compatibility in the construction

* Field effect was first investigated by Shockley in 1952.

of integrated circuits, it would seem that multiple-diffusion, planar, epitaxial techniques could be used with advantage here. Both integrated and discrete field effect transistors are now of this kind.

Integrated FET's*

Figure 4.4 shows how an n-type channel FET can be produced by diffusion in an epitaxial layer on an n^+-type silicon substrate. In the figure, it will be seen that gate 1 surrounds the active element and gate 2 is in the shape of an annulus. It is thus possible to arrange for the evaporated pattern of conductors, deposited on the oxide layer,

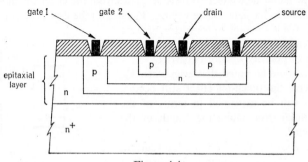

Figure 4.4

to connect the two gates and so bring about the constriction of the drain current.

Alternatively, in some applications, the two gates may be operated independently of each other.

The input capacitance is a function of the area of the junction between the gate and the channel. For this reason, one of the gates, perhaps gate 1, may be connected to the source, and the input signal applied to gate 2. Used in this way, a typical input capacitance of 30 picofarads can be reduced to about 10 picofarads. Although the input resistance, R_{gs}, remains high (about 1000 megohms), the gain of the device is understandably reduced. This gain is assessed in terms of the mutual conductance, g_m [$= (\partial I_d / \partial V_{gs})$ at a constant V_{ds}]. Typically, g_m is of the order of 2 milliamps per volt (2000

* Field effect transistors.

micromhos). Typical applications of FET's require a high g_m and low V_p at some reasonable, high drain current, I_d. In order to obtain this, it is necessary to have a high length-to-width ratio for the channel. This is commonly in excess of 100. The characteristics of two typical devices are shown in table 4.1.

Table 4.1

Type	Channel width (microns)	Length (microns)	I_d (mA)	g_m (mA/V)	V_p (V)	C_{gs} (pF)	Input leakage current (nA)
ZFT 12	3	360	1	1·5	1·5	30	3
ZFT 14	6	720	6	3·0	5·0	50	3

In the same way that a model or equivalent circuit was used to explain the behaviour of a conventional transistor in a practical circuit, so that action of a field effect transistor can be understood with the aid of the model of figure 4.5.

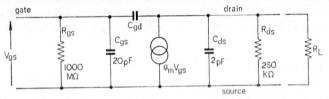

Figure 4.5

From the model, it can be seen that the input impedance becomes reduced at high frequencies, owing to the shunting effect of C_{gs}. Care must also be taken in integrated circuitry to avoid the use of a resistor whose value is outside the range of values which is easily obtainable. For example, it is often necessary to bias the gate so that an alternating potential applied to it does not result in it being forward biased over part of the cycle. Methods of bias must be examined which do not resort to using high resistances.

Also, figure 4.5 illustrates the capacitance which shunts the output. This is usually less important than the input capacitance, particularly where the output resistance, R_{ds}, is small. There is also a gate-drain feedback capacitance, C_{gd}, in the figure, which is typically of the order of 5 picofarads or less.

Temperature effects, too, play a part in the design of FET amplifiers. The intrinsic leakage current across the gate junction increases
logarithmically with temperature. A typical current of 1 nanoamp at
room temperature will have increased to the order of several
hundred nanoamps at a temperature of 100°C, although this is
dependent on the resistivity of the silicon used (typically 0·5 to 5
ohm-cm). In addition, the mobility of the majority carriers, responsible for conduction, increases as the temperature of the material
is raised. Hence the resistivity of the channel is reduced, and so, at
high temperatures, the drain current, which is proportional to it, is
reduced also. This reduction is of the same order of magnitude as the
increase in collector current of a conventional transistor over the
same temperature range. This fact and the known thermal advantages
of single chip construction suggest further that FET's and conventional transistors may, with advantage, be used together in integrated, linear amplifier circuits. Also, the gate capacitance and the
pinch-off voltage fall with increasing temperature, although these
changes are sufficiently small to be unimportant for many applications.

p-type channel FET's
The explanation of field effect devices has, so far, been based on the
use of n-type channel FET's. It is equally possible to use a p-type
channel with an n-type gate. In such a case, however, the gate must
be biased positively with respect to the source. Considerations of
isolation suggest that n-type channel FET's will be better suited to
integrated circuits than p-type ones. It should be noted that a p-type
channel FET can be distinguished, in a circuit diagram, by the
reverse direction of the arrow on the gate terminal of the symbol.*

FET amplifier circuits
For stable operation, there must be a continuous path from the gate
to the source, as shown in figure 4.6. The resistor which is provided
for this purpose inevitably shunts the input impedance.

The limitations which this discrete circuit presents to integration
are the high capacitance in the source circuit and the gate resistor.

* See figure 4.6.

The collector load, R_L, is provided so that the drain current can cause an output voltage to be produced across it. From figure 4.5, it can be shown that the voltage gain, a_v, of an amplifier circuit of this kind is given approximately by

$$a_v = g_m R_L \qquad (4.1)$$

Higher input impedance is obtained with 'source follower' circuits, such as that shown in figure 4.7. The voltage gain of such circuits is often just less than unity. In figure 4.7, the amplifier has an overall gain which is higher than this, owing to the gain of the transistor amplifier which follows the FET.

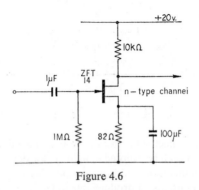

Figure 4.6

Except for the presence of the high resistance, R_g, this circuit is more suitable for single chip construction. This last difficulty can be overcome by replacing this resistor by a forward-biased diode, whose slope resistance is typically about 25 ohms at room temperature when a current of 1 milliamp is passing through it. However, its slope resistance is inversely proportional to the current which flows through it. Hence, at the typical gate current of 1 nanoamp, its resistance is 25 megohms. It should be clear to the reader by now that it is much easier to produce a planar diode of this kind on a silicon chip than it is to produce high resistors of the order of 25 megohms. Thus, in integrated circuits using FET's, diodes are generally used for bias. However, the resistance temperature coefficients of such

components are higher than for their conventional resistor counter-
parts. This problem can be minimised; for one of the principal
advantages of single chip construction is to ensure that all components are in good thermal contact. Then, although absolute re-

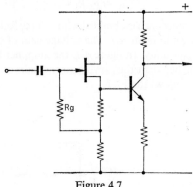

Figure 4.7

sistance values will change, the ratios of these values tend to change
much less.

Recently, field effect transistors have been introduced* in which
the input junction can be exposed to light. These devices are sensitive
to infra-red illumination, and it is now possible to use this method
with integrated circuits to produce integrated, low-noise, photocell
amplifiers.

Metal oxide silicon transistors

Field effect transistors were introduced as a solution to a specific
problem: that of the low input impedance of conventional transistor
amplifiers, even where the emitter–follower mode of operation was
employed. In solving this problem, other problems are posed. The
high input capacitance of conventional amplifiers is important, but
not vitally so, in designing an amplifier to have a wide pass band of
frequencies, because of the low input resistance which shunts it. The
field effect transistor has a very high input resistance, so that the

* By Siliconix, Inc., California.

small input capacitance shunting it, which the device possesses, becomes decisive in limiting its frequency response. A lesser problem is that the input junction of an FET must always be reverse biased, or the input impedance falls when this junction is called upon to pass current. Some of these objections to FET's are overcome in another field effect device, the metal-oxide silicon transistor, the development of which could not take place until the introduction of planar techniques.

Depletion-type MOS* transistors

The MOS transistor of figure 4.8 operates in a way which is very similar to the FET. It consists of an n-channel which has been selectively diffused into a p-type substrate. Connections to the ends

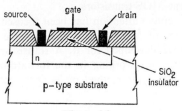

Figure 4.8

of this channel form the source and the drain. However, this layer is covered by an insulating oxide layer, as shown in the figure, and a metallic gate electrode is deposited on it. Thus, MOS transistors are hybrid devices. A potential applied to the gate induces a charge on the channel which causes a depletion layer to be formed, in a similar way to that described in the FET. However, since this gate electrode is well insulated by the oxide layer, the input resistance is particularly high, of the order of 10^{14} ohms, and is shunted by an input capacitance which depends on the geometry of the gate and on the thickness and dielectric constant of the oxide layer. This capacitance is typically of the order of 5 picofarads.

If there are no pinholes in the oxide layer, it may be expected that the input resistance should be of the order of 10^{15} ohms, but the resistivity of the encapsulation is usually low enough to reduce it to the

* Metal-oxide-silicon.

order of 10^{12} ohms. Thus, the encapsulation resistivity is commonly the deciding factor in the input resistance of the transistor.

When the polarity of the input voltage is changed to produce forward bias, then, unlike the FET, and owing to the insulation of the gate, no input current flows. Forward bias, however, does tend to enhance the output drain current. The characteristics of the transistor are somewhat similar to those shown in figure 4.2, except that equally spaced curves can be drawn for positive as well as negative gate voltages. The device shown in figure 4.8 is intended primarily as a depletion type MOS transistor. It possesses the usual pinch-off type of characteristic, with an output impedance above the pinch-off voltage of the order of 100 kilohms.

Enhancement-type MOS transistors

Recently, considerable attention has been focused on the current-enhancement type of MOS transistor, and some very interesting circuits have been developed for it. A transistor of this kind is designed primarily for working in the forward-biased condition. A typical example of the method of its construction is shown in figure 4.9.

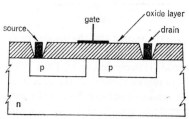

Figure 4.9

The p-type regions to which connections are made, as source and drain, each make distinct p–n junctions with the substrate, so that these parts of the device can be regarded as a low-current gain transistor which is non-conducting. However, when the gate electrode is negatively biased, a positive charge is induced in the region between the source and the drain, so that this region is inverted from being n-type material to act as though it had been doped with a p-type impurity. The positive charge is said to have produced an enhancement effect. Current passes between source and drain without any gate current flowing. This is because the gate electrode is isolated from the silicon slice by the oxide layer. With a suitable geometry for the p-type regions and the substrate, the gate electrode need not be very large, so that there is only a small input capacitance associated with it.

There is a small threshold voltage, which must be applied to the gate before the enhancement region is continuous between source and drain, but, when this has been exceeded, the current which flows is due to the carriers from the p-type regions. Hence the device can be considered to act as a p-channel MOS transistor. n-channel devices also exist, and the applications of each of these will be discussed in later chapters.

Typical parameters for an enhancement-type MOS transistor are as follows.

General Microelectronics type 1004

R_{gs}	10^{14} ohms	R_{ds}	40 kilohms
C_{gs}	7·5 picofarads	C_{ds}	2·0 picofarads
C_{gd}	2·5 picofarads	g_m	1000 micromhos

Comparison of MOS transistors and junction-type FET's
The advantages of junction-type FET's are their stability and good, low-noise performance. However, they do not readily lend themselves to integrated techniques, whereas the MOS transistors have a more simple method of construction which is compatible with silicon chip, monolithic fabrication. Their higher input impedance, whilst sometimes advantageous, also implies a long *RC* time constant, so that transient operation is adversely affected and switching speed therefore reduced.

Comparison of unipolar and bipolar transistors
MOS transistors are available as enhancement devices, when they are usually p-type, and as depletion devices, when they are more commonly n-type; although in each case both types are manufactured. Present developments seem to favour enhancement-type transistors.

When operated as linear amplifiers, the p-channel transistors are usually less suitable, owing to greater drift of voltage levels. This is probably due to charge centres, perhaps sodium ions, in the oxide layer, which are affected only by a positive, induced charge.

MOS devices only occupy a small area of the surface of a slice, less than that required for bipolar transistors. Also, special isolation techniques are less frequently required, since the substrate itself is not part of the device, and it is thus self-isolating. It is thus easier to accommodate larger numbers of elements on a slice.

Plate 5 shows three enhancement-mode MOS transistors on a single slice. The three gate electrodes are on the left-hand side of the slice. The area of the whole slice is similar to that of the slice in plate 2 which carried only one transistor. It should be noted that no isolation lands are required between the transistors.

CHAPTER 5

Logical Circuits

Introduction

The development of the electronics industry was based at first on the domestic radio market. Hence, electronics engineers, in the years before the war, came to regard linear voltage and power amplifiers as by far the most common types of circuit. Since then, and particularly since the introduction of transistors, switching circuits have come into greater use, initially in digital computers. In switching circuits, the output of the circuit can assume one of two states, depending either on the voltage levels at a number of input points, or on the application of pulses to the circuit. The logical functions which such circuits can be said to carry out, and which obviously depend on the arrangement of the components in them, will be discussed in this chapter. Nowadays, complete sections of the industrial electronics industry find as much or more use for logical circuits than for linear amplifiers.

The advent of microelectronics has shifted the emphasis from the component as the unit of construction to the circuit. Thus, the trend has been to consider simple electronic circuits as the building bricks of larger systems, and to concentrate on the use of reliable modules of this kind, rather than on producing circuits from individual re-sistors, capacitors, and the like. Nowhere has this trend been more readily received than in the use of logical circuits, where the engineer had already been trained to think in terms of the circuit as the funda-mental unit of design. For this reason, considerable attention must be given to microelectronic logical circuits, to the principles on which they operate, and to their applications.

Logical circuits were also particularly appropriate for the imple-mentation of microelectronics, not solely owing to the associated history of modular circuitry, but also because they seldom used high

or low resistance values, which were difficult and costly to manufacture, and because capacitors were only rarely used and inductors
never required.

Parameters of logical elements

When discussing linear circuits, terms such as h_{oe}, h_{fe}, and h_{ie} are
frequently quoted by the manufacturer, and expected by the circuit
designer. What parameters are necessary for digital circuits? The
parameters of logical elements will be discussed here, but clearly the
parameters of linear integrated circuits will not be very different.

Firstly, the function of the circuit must be defined. This and subsequent chapters will deal extensively with this point. There must also
be interconnection rules or loading tables stating the fan-in and fan-
out of the element.

Secondly, the operating conditions must be defined. This includes
temperature range for use and storage, and the tolerance of the
supply voltage which is used. It is important that these operating
conditions are applicable for the loading range which is specified.

Finally, it is often the case that the manufacturer provides a circuit diagram of the element and states nominal values for the
passive components. These, like the circuit diagrams in this book, are
inherited from the days of discrete component circuits. They do not
completely show the operation of the circuit, owing to the distributed
nature of the circuit elements and the presence of parasites. The
circuit values are very seldom guaranteed, since changes in the
diffusion process will result in them all changing proportionately.
Hence, where the manufacturer specifies performance tests, such as
rise and fall times and static tests, these are not dependent on
absolute values of components but on the relative values being held
to specification.

Logical conventions

Thin-film techniques can be used to produce logical circuits in which
the transistors are produced separately. A typical example of this
kind is shown in figure 2.2. Assume that this circuit has two inputs,
A and B, at which voltages can be applied with respect to the common
line, and that these voltages can independently take one of two

values. For instance, if the supply voltage to the circuit is 3 volts, it may be that the two input levels are zero and $+3$ volts. Now, it is convenient to designate these two levels as '0' and '1'. If the more negative of the levels, in this case the zero voltage, is designated '1', then such an arrangement is said to follow a negative logical convention. Similarly, if the more positive level is taken as '1', a positive logical convention is said to apply.

Functions of logical elements

Using a negative logical convention, it can be seen that if either (or both) of the inputs is a '0' then the positive voltage level which corresponds to '0' will turn on the n–p–n transistor in figure 2.2, so that the output potential will fall to that of the common line, that is, to the '1' level. This can be summarised as shown in table 5.1.

Table 5.1

A	B	Output
0	0	1
0	1	1
1	0	1
1	1	0

From the table, it can be seen that the output is '1' for all those cases except that in which both A and B are '1'. The function of the circuit is thus said to be that of 'not-and' or 'nand', and is written as $\overline{AB}$, where the bar stands for the 'not', and the AB represents the 'A and B' part of the function. De Morgan* has shown that the expression can also be written as $\bar{A} + \bar{B}$ (not A or not B). The 'or' function introduced here will also be met using the same circuit but arranged for a positive logical convention.

In this positive convention, $+3$ volts is represented by '1' and, wherever a '1' exists at one or more inputs, the transistor is turned on, so that the output is at the '0' level. This is shown in table 5.2.

The table shows that the function of the circuit is $\bar{A}\bar{B}$, since the only condition which results in a '1' at the output is the presence of '0' at each input. This may also be written as $\overline{A + B}$, since the output

* See appendix A.

E

Table 5.2

A	B	Output
0	0	1
0	1	0
1	0	0
1	1	0

is not present when A or B is present. It is said to be a 'not-or' or 'nor' element.

It should be noted that in this argument the term 'or' is taken to include the condition 'and', so that 'or' is said to be 'an inclusive or', including the 'and' condition.

This circuit, then, is a typical building brick for a logical system. It would, however, be a more convenient unit if it performed a function more closely related to our own thought processes. We tend to think in terms of the combinations and choices which are permitted to us ('and' and 'or') rather than of those combinations ('nand' and 'nor') which are excluded. This can be arranged using combinations of a number of these elements.

Logical symbols

At once, this suggests that complex circuit diagrams must be drawn where a great deal of interconnection is involved. This is avoided by using a logical symbol for the basic element, so that logical diagrams, rather than circuit diagrams, will be required. There is, unfortunately,

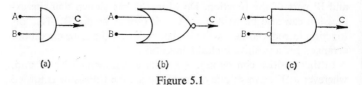

(a)   (b)   (c)

Figure 5.1

more than one system which is used for this purpose. An American standard symbol is shown in figure 5.1a. The symbol itself does not imply any definite logical convention, and one is left to discover this from the declared function of the output, C. The American Military Standard 806ʙ is shown in figures 5.1b and 5.1c. The symbol in (b) is to be used when the function is 'nor', that is, with a positive logical convention. The symbol in (c) is applicable to a negative convention, when its function is 'nand'.

The significance of these symbols is best understood by using the terms 'high' and 'low' to indicate voltage levels. The logical convention is not compromised by this, for it can then be applied by assigning the '1' level to one or other of these states.

The precise meaning of figure 5.1c is that of 'and'. This is indicated by the shape of the symbol. However, the inputs, A and B, have circles adjoining the symbol, indicating that the inputs are low when the output (with no circle) is high. This can be summarised as 'C is high when A *and* B are low'. Similarly, in figure 5.1b, the symbol shape represents the function 'or' so that here 'C is low when A *or* B is high'. From de Morgan's theorem, it can be seen that these symbols in fact represent the same function.

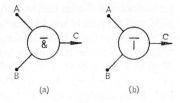

One implication of this symbolism which is not stated explicitly in the Standard is that, when the output lead of a symbol is

Figure 5.2

represented as high, it is best to take it to the input of another symbol whose input is represented as high. Connection between low outputs and inputs is made in a similar way. Thus, if a series of elements which have identical functions is connected together, they can be represented alternately by the functions shown in figures 5.1b and 5.1c.

Finally, there is the British Standard 530, Supplement No. 5 (1962). There are two symbols here, that for 'nand' in figure 5.2a and that for 'nor' in figure 5.2b.

In all of these symbols, the power supply lines are omitted, and the symbol is intended to show the logical function of the circuit, rather than the interconnection of the components. For this reason, it is important to note that *any* electronic* circuit which performs a given function will be illustrated by the same logical symbol, no

---

* The same symbol also applies to non-electronic systems with the same function, e.g. mechanical and pneumatic logic systems.

matter whether valves, transistors, or tunnel diodes are used for this purpose.

Design considerations

Before considering some typical logical circuits in detail, it is worthwhile summarising some of the design considerations of these circuits. A summary of their relative merits will also appear later in the chapter. The problems which are about to be outlined will have been faced already by the integrated circuit designer, but the applications engineer who uses such circuits should be well aware of the design problems of the units he uses and the implications of compromise which these problems have placed on the designer.

For silicon chip circuits, the circuit designer will have favoured transistors and diodes rather than resistors since they exhibit high yield and frequently use less surface area. The resistance range of resistors is also limited. In addition, the designer will prefer to use low voltages, since the breakdown voltages of integrated circuits are often small. In order to obtain high speed, transistors should not be permitted to saturate heavily. These considerations may result in logic levels which are separated by only a small potential difference so that it may not be easy to use these levels with peripheral equipment. Also, if the system is installed in an environment which is subject to electrical noise, and the logic swing is small, the reliability of the system may be degraded owing to this noise.

Considerations of propagation delay and power dissipation are often interconnected and when these points have been considered there will still be the problems of organisation – of how to make contact between perhaps 10 to 15 points on the silicon slice and the 'outside world'. These are problems of packaging and of multi-layer printed circuits. They are intensely practical, for these methods must neither reduce the reliability of the system unduly, nor increase its size or its cost to an undesirable extent.

Temperature range

Digital integrated circuits are usually specified for the range $-55°C$ to $+125°C$. However, some high-speed circuits, with high dissipation, cannot be provided with encapsulation which has a sufficiently low thermal resistance to operate over this wide temperature range. They are thus usually specified over a narrower range. Also, since a narrower temperature range can be offered for these and indeed for any elements, with a reduced testing programme, such elements are frequently available more cheaply.

Transistor–resistor logic

The simple TRL* element of figure 2.2 may have a number of input limbs, and a number of similar elements may be connected to the output of any particular element. What is the maximum number which may be so connected? The number of input limbs is termed the fan-in of an element. The limitation which the fan-in of an element imposes on system design is not so great a problem as the fan-out, the number of elements which may be connected to the output of an element. This implies that, when other elements are so connected, current will be required to turn them on, and that this current must be supplied without materially altering the potential of the driving collector. Hence, some degree of saturation must often be tolerated, so that loading can take place without changing the collector potential. This saturation is bound to limit the speed of operation of the element.

Impedance problems connected with the value of the input resistors, the fan-out, and the propagation delay of an element are all interconnected, so that the design of an element is a matter of compromise. A typical fan-out is in the range 4 to 10, although with most systems of integrated circuits the fan-out tends to be rather low about 5, unless special output circuits are designed. This is because the voltages used are lower, and hence the power dissipated is very often smaller than with discrete circuitry.

The propagation delay through a logical element is of considerable importance, since the timing of logical systems may have to be accurately controlled. This delay may be estimated by connecting a number, perhaps ten, of these elements in tandem and finding the overall delay and dividing by the number of elements to obtain the average delay. At high temperatures, the propagation delay can become greater, typically doubling for 100°C rise.

* Transistor–resistor logic, also known as RTL.

TRL circuits

The circuit shown in figure 5.3 is of some interest, since it is typical of integrated circuitry. Figure 5.3a shows the circuit using an American convention, and figure 5.3b shows the British standard symbols for the same circuit. The construction of a single TRL element is well within the capability of microelectronic techniques, since only one active element is involved and there are few passive elements. Thus, compound circuits of this kind are often encountered on a single substrate or a silicon chip.

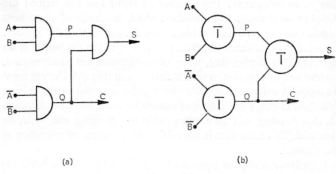

(a)   (b)

Figure 5.3

If a positive logical convention is employed, the logic at P will be $\overline{A + B}$ or $\overline{A}\overline{B}$, and that at Q, $\overline{\overline{A} + \overline{B}}$. By de Morgan's theorems, the logic at Q simplifies to AB. Since the points P and Q are inputs to the final element, the output at S is $\overline{\overline{A}\overline{B} + AB}$, which simplifies to $\overline{A}B + A\overline{B}$. The complete circuit is that of a half-adder. S is '1' when the sum of A and B is '1'. C is the carry from this addition. Circuits of this kind are used as parallel adders in the arithmetic units of computers.

When considering logical conventions, the two conventions already outlined led to discussing the 'nor' and 'nand' functions. However, it may sometimes be useful to consider two further conventions, known as the two mixed conventions.

If a positive level is taken as '1' at the input to a TRL element, and a negative level as '1' at its output, then a truth table will show that the element behaves as an 'or' element. This is because the transistor is turned on by a positive level on any of the resistive limbs of its input circuit, thus causing the output to assume the more negative state. But this, at the output, is taken as '1'. Thus a '1' (in negative logic) is produced by a '1' (in positive logic) at one or more of the input limbs, and this is the function of an 'or' element.

Similarly, an 'and' function is appropriate if the input convention is negative, and the output is in positive logic. If one element, considered as operating in a positive-in negative-out convention, is

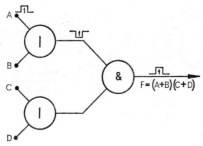

Figure 5.4

followed by one of the opposite type, then the input of the first and the output of the second are both in positive logic, and the function of the complete circuit is the same as if positive logic had been assumed throughout. In this way, it is sometimes much easier to visualise the design of a logical system than if the Boolean function had to be written down and simplified for each stage of logic. Thus, in figure 5.4, where the levels are indicated by pulse symbols, the output, F, is in positive logic.

An expression such as the function, F, is known as a maxterm, whereas the function, AB + CD, is a minterm. Thus, it should be remembered that a positive logic convention, over two stages, favours maxterm-type expressions.

Similarly, if the input of a stage is in negative logic and the output of the following stage is in the same convention, the function of the two stages can be visualised as in figure 5.5. Here the output is a minterm-type expression.

The functions of these circuits can easily be checked by considering each element to have the functions 'nor' in figure 5.4 and 'nand' in figure 5.5.* It should not be thought, however, that minterms cannot be handled in positive logic, or maxterms when a negative convention is employed. For example, using the function of figure 5.4, $(A + B)(C + D)$, this may be written as $AC + BC + AD + BD$, which is then suitable for negative logic circuits.

Unfortunately, it is not so easy to expand minterms into con-

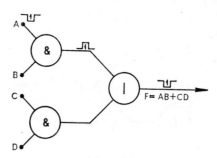

Figure 5.5

venient maxterms, so that it is more common to find TRL systems that use negative (nand) logic than a positive (nor) convention.

The principles which have just been outlined are of particular interest when using integrated circuits. For instance, if negative logic is used, an 'and' element can easily be constructed using two transistors. This is shown in figure 5.6.

The circuit acts as an 'and' element, but, if a further limb is connected at P, the 'or' function can be introduced. Circuits of this kind can easily be produced as single elements with a suitable fan-in at P.

The resistors in each of the input limbs are used to increase the

---

* Here, the case of n–p–n transistors has been examined, since these are more common than p–n–p devices in integrated circuits. However, if p–n–p transistors are used, the functions of the elements in each of the conventions is changed, e.g. negative logic produces the 'nor' function.

input impedance of the element, so that a number of similar elements may be connected to one driving element. Thus, the driving element can have a high fan-out. One problem with this type of circuit is that if the input resistors are low, the fan-out may be low, and also there will be the chance that one of the driven circuits, having a lower input resistance than the others, will rob the driving element of the

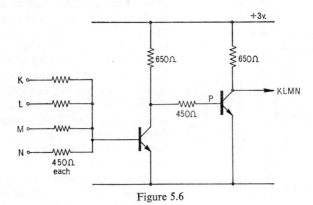

Figure 5.6

majority of its output current. This 'current hogging' is a particular disadvantage of directly coupled transistor logic (DCTL) circuits, in which these resistors are omitted and direct connection made from the collector of the driving stage to the bases of the driven ones.

It has been explained that one of the design problems of TRL elements is that a fan-in and fan-out is required which is comparable with discrete circuits. This requires resistor ratios with only a few per cent tolerance. Thus the thin-film approach is to be preferred, if this circuit is to be made in integrated form.

Modified, directly coupled transistor logic

The circuit of figure 5.6 is typical of thin-film circuits. If a silicon chip circuit is to be used, it may be modified, if it is remembered that transistors are readily available in this type of circuit. For this reason, the circuit of figure 5.7 is often described as a modified DCTL system.

Is this circuit liable to current hogging? In monolithic, integrated circuits, it may be argued, the transistors are simultaneously produced as an integral part of the circuit, and thus they can all be expected to have similar characteristics to each other and are subject

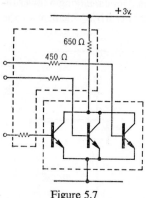

Figure 5.7

to the same sort of control as the resistors which form the input limbs. Thus, current problems are minimised. Further, it is the case that circuits using low values of resistance are characterised by higher speed and higher dissipation than comparable elements with higher resistances. For example, if the circuit of figure 5.7 used integrated, planar transistors, it would dissipate about 12 milliwatts and have a propagation time of about 10 nanoseconds. If the input resistors were each increased to, say,
1·5 kilohms, and the collector resistor increased to about 3·5 kilohms, the dissipation would then be reduced to 3 milliwatts and the propagation time could be expected to increase to 25 nanoseconds.*

The broken line in figure 5.7 shows that two lands would be required in fabricating the circuit in monolithic form.

Resistor–capacitor transistor logic

Current hogging is most easily avoided if large input resistors are used in the logical circuit. However, this leads to an increase in the storage time of the circuit, since charge cannot easily be removed when the transistor is turned off, owing to the increase in time constant of the base–emitter circuit. Also, increase in base resistance must also lead to an increase in the collector resistor, and this makes it difficult to provide current which the large output voltage requires

---

* SGS-Fairchild's micrologic range is an example of a system in which there are high-speed medium-power, and medium-speed low-power elements.

for the stray capacitances associated with the output circuit. These objections can be overcome by the use of shunt capacitors for the input limbs. This is illustrated in figure 5.8.

When T_1 and T_2 are off, T_3 is turned on, owing to the high voltage, V_c, at the collectors of T_1 and T_2. If now T_1 conducts, the voltage at

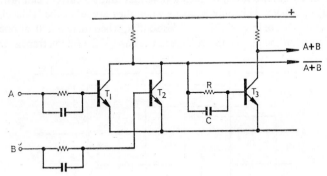

Figure 5.8

its collector falls to the saturation level, V_s. Thus, if R_s is the saturation resistance of T_1, and I_c is its collector current,

$$I_c R_s = V_c - V_s$$

Thus, if V_c is much greater than V_s, and the base drive to T_1 is adequate, I_c will be nearly independent of V_s, and hence current hogging will not take place. In practice, this is never quite achieved, but if the RC time-constant is large compared with the rise time of the signal, the rise time of the driven unit will be fixed by R and C. Although the capacitor, C, which dynamically couples the stages assists in switching the stages, it makes the system more sensitive to noise 'turn-on' voltages than TRL.

Diode–transistor logic

The resistors in a TRL element perform the gating function of the element, and the transistor inverts it. Since in monolithic circuits it is easier to construct diodes than resistors, it is reasonable to suppose that it would be advantageous to replace the resistors in the input limbs by diodes. This is illustrated in the DTL* element shown in figure 5.9.

If positive logic is used, the input diodes, D_1 to D_3, may be assumed to act with R_1 as an 'and' gate, so that the logic at this point in the circuit is ABC. This is because a '1' will only appear here if all the input diodes are taken to such a potential that no current can flow through them. This only happens when they are all at the '1' level. D_4 and D_5 are level-shifting diodes so that, when there is a '0' at one or more of the inputs, the voltage at the base of the silicon transistor

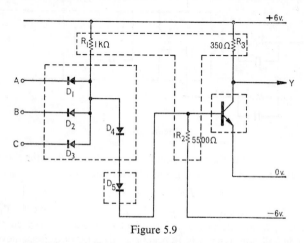

Figure 5.9

is not sufficient to turn it on. The output at Y, therefore, is a '1'. When there is a '1' at X, the transistor is turned on, so that there is a '0' at Y. The whole system, then, is thus a 'nand' element in positive logic. By similar arguments, it can be shown to be a 'nor' element if negative logic is used. This DTL system is sometimes known as low-level logic (LLL).

The broken lines in figure 5.9 show that four lands would be used in making the circuit in monolithic form.

In order to obtain a reasonable fan-out from the circuit, there must be an adequate drive to the transistor. This will usually require

* Diode–transistor logic.

a higher supply potential than for other logical systems if R_1 is not to be unduly low. Therefore, it is usual to have a relatively high supply potential associated with quite high values for R_1 and R_2. This may tend to reduce speed, owing to the time constants associated with these resistors. Thus, a compromise among fan-out, propagation delay, and power dissipation must be made in the design of this circuit.

DTL circuits, having a high supply voltage, are less liable to noise interference than other systems. This is particularly true if R_2 is

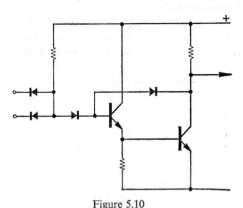

Figure 5.10

returned to a negative supply, although this may result in further reduction of switching speed and increase of power dissipation. The input diodes provide very good insulation from other elements connected to a common source, so that current hogging does not occur. The level-shifting diodes, D_4 and D_5, store the charge which is injected into the base of the transistor when it is turned off. One of the design problems of this circuit is to ensure that this charge neutralises the base-emitter charge before the diodes themselves revert to the high-impedance state.

For the reasons which have been explained, the input diodes must be high-speed fast-recovery diodes, and the level-shifting diodes must be slow-recovery types. Thus, as pointed out in chapter 3, a base–collector junction diffusion could be used for the input logic diodes, and a base–emitter junction diffusion for the level-shifting diodes.

The circuit which has just been described contains no precautions against saturation. It is possible to use a diode-controlled feedback amplifier to protect the circuit against saturation and so reduce the propagation delay, but care must be taken to ensure that the storage time of the diode does not mask this effect. A typical circuit of this kind is shown in figure 5.10.

Transistor–transistor logic

Figure 5.11 shows the basic TTL* element. TTL is a natural development of DTL, for it retains all of its advantages and introduces other advantages also. The system is well suited to monolithic techniques,

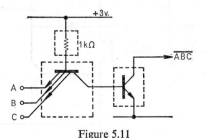

Figure 5.11

for, as can be seen from the figure, there are only three isolation lands. Speed was limited in DTL by charge stored in the diodes. Since these are omitted here, it will be appreciated that TTL has a low propagation delay, and is an improvement on a comparable DTL element. The multiple-emitter transistor will act as a low-impedance discharge path for charge stored in the other transistor.

Current robbing can occur in TTL owing to the variation between elements in the base-emitter potential of the common-base mode transistor. This is not so severe a problem as the current hogging of DCTL.

The potentials at the input need only swing a few tens of millivolts, and hence it is possible to design TTL circuits for very low power

* Transistor–transistor logic.

dissipation. Logic levels are usually defined which are greater than this, since logic levels which are close together are generally undesirable. However, fan-out and noise rejection are not particularly good. For these reasons, manufacturers have attempted to modify TTL elements to improve their performance in these respects; and also because, potentially, TTL seems to offer very many of the

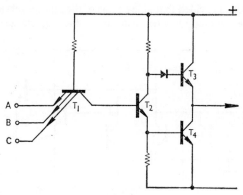

Figure 5.12

requirements of a good logical system for integrated circuits. One of these modifications is shown in figure 5.12.

Consider the case when the inputs, A and B, are at the positive logic level, so that no current is flowing at these points. If C now goes positive, T_1 ceases to conduct and this turns off T_2, so that T_3 is turned on. Then, since the load is connected through a transistor turning on, a good fan-out can be obtained, particularly since T_3 is an emitter follower. When C goes negative, T_2 and T_4 conduct, so that charge stored in the load has a low time-constant path to earth.

Current–mode logic*

In the search for faster logical elements, we have seen that recurring problems of charge storage have limited the speed of operation. Current–mode logic is a system in which a transistor is switched

* Also known as emitter-coupled transistor logic.

between two well-defined voltage levels in such a way that it never saturates but remains in the active or current mode of operation. Figure 5.13 illustrates a typical CML* system.

Assume that a current, I, flows in the resistor, R_1, so that a potential, IR_1, develops across it. Contributions to this current come from T_1, T_2, T_3, and T_4. The base potential of T_4 is fixed by the reference potential, so that the current through T_4 is determined by V_{ref} and IR_1. Provided that at least one of the input levels is positive, so that the corresponding transistor is conducting, a large part of the

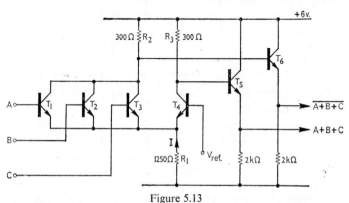

Figure 5.13

current, I, will pass through it, developing a voltage across R_2. Thus in terms of positive logic, the function of the voltage at the collector of T_3, and hence at the output of T_6, is that of a 'nor' element, since this level is only positive when none of the inputs are positive. Under these conditions, T_4 is just conducting and the level at its collector is positive, so that T_5 gives a positive-level output.

However, should all the signal inputs be at the '0' level, then the current, I, cannot pass through the input transistors and it is switched through T_4. A suitable choice of reference voltage† and of I and R_1 can ensure that T_4 does not saturate, and since the emitters of T_5 and T_6 can follow their bases they do not saturate either. Since

* Current–mode logic.
† Midway between the logic levels.

the input to T_5 is positive so long as at least one input is positive, the function at its output is the 'or' function.

From this, it will be seen that the advantages of CML are the high fan-out afforded by the emitter followers and their closely defined logic levels, and high speed due to the non-saturating or current mode of operation. Also, the nature of the design makes it easy to provide two output functions from one integrated circuit, as shown in the figure. One disadvantage is the relative complexity of the circuit, and, although this may seem to suggest low yields in manufacture, in fact the ratio of the resistors is more important than their absolute values, so that this drawback is not so important. Also, it will be seen that a reference voltage is required to ensure that the circuit operates in the current mode. However, in practice a number of elements may be operated from the same reference source.

The logic levels associated with CML circuits are sometimes difficult to use to drive other ancillary equipment. For example, in the circuit of figure 5.13, the reference voltage would be 4·8 volts and the logic levels 5·4 volts and 4·2 volts.

Thus, CML is used where rapid switching at relatively high power levels and the advantages of high fan-out and of noise immunity are more important than the problems of the complexity of the system. This system together with TTL seems to offer most hope for future integrated-circuit developments at high speed.

Complementary transistor logic

CTL* has only recently become available, owing to early difficulties in producing both n–p–n and p–n–p transistors of reasonable current gain on a single chip. Typical propagation delay for a circuit similar to that shown in figure 5.14 is in the range 2 to 6 nanoseconds. These elements are intended for use in the central processors of high-speed computers, and in common with other high-speed circuits have high dissipation.

The function of the circuit shown in figure 5.14 is ABC in positive logic. It will be seen that current through R_1 is redistributed throughout a switching transition, either flowing through the p–n–p transistors or the n–p–n transistor. This eliminates the threshold

* Complementary transistor logic.

F

delay associated with switching and is responsible for the high speeds
associated with CTL. In this system, the propagation delay may be
accounted for as a result of redistribution of charge between the
transistors, which is very much less than a delay which occurs in a
saturating circuit.

In any viable logic system, the functions 'and', 'or', and 'invert'
must be available. With CTL, the 'or' function is available without
additional circuitry, since it can be produced by direct connection of

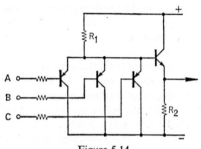

Figure 5.14

outputs. This is sometimes called a 'wired-or' facility. The 'invert'
function must also be added although it is often not necessary to
invert logic levels until after two or three operations.

The noise immunity of CTL is particularly good, since the basic
CTL circuit has an emitter-follower output which has low impedance,
and the absence of threshold and storage delays permit the use of a
large logic voltage swing.

FET logic elements

Owing to their small physical size,* FET elements should not be
omitted in a discussion of logic modules. The commercial production
of MOS logic elements† has shown that chip size reduction can be
effected if passive elements are also replaced by MOS devices. This is
possible since, as explained earlier, the field effect transistor is a

* Less than one-twentieth of that of an integrated-circuit transistor.
† Initially by General Microelectronics, Inc., now Philco Ltd.

voltage-controlled resistor. This is particularly attractive with digital elements, since systems such as DCTL can be developed with many more active elements than passive ones. Also, the traditional problem of current hogging, associated with DCTL, can no longer apply if MOS devices are used.

The principal drawback with field effect logic elements is one of speed. The gate capacitance and resistance ensure a long input time-constant, so that a typical operating speed is of the order of 1 megahertz.

Figure 5.15 shows how these elements may be used in a logic gate.

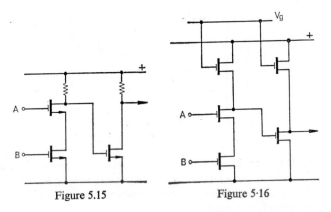

Figure 5.15   Figure 5·16

When the inputs A and B are both made positive, then drain current can flow in both input transistors, so lowering the voltage on the gate of the output transistor. Thus, the output level is made more positive. The element thus acts as an 'and' gate in positive logic.

Notice, in the figure, the arrowheads on the transistor symbols. These show the source electrode, and their direction identifies the transistors as being n-channel. Where there is no cause for confusion, these arrows may be omitted.

Figure 5.16 shows how the resistors in the gate may be replaced by MOS devices. The logical operation of the gate is unchanged. The extra supply potential, V_g, is necessary to bring the MOS transistors, which are replacing the resistors, into the enhancement mode, so that they are conducting. It is therefore possible to use this voltage line as a control for the resistance of these elements.

One of the attractive features of FET logic elements is the possibility of using complementary circuitry, in which both p-channel and n-channel devices are employed. The p-channel device requires a negative gate potential to permit conduction in the channel, whereas an n-channel transistor requires a positive gate potential.

Figure 5.17 shows a complementary switching circuit analogous to the complementary emitter follower using bipolar transistors. In this type of circuit, the standby dissipation is very low, as conduction

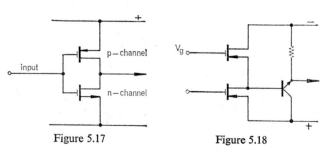

Figure 5.17   Figure 5.18

only takes place during a transition between input levels. Since in each transition one or other of the transistors will be biased into conduction, the input time-constant is reduced, and hence the speed of operation is increased.

The high input impedance of MOS transistors implies a large fan-out between MOS devices, but where low output impedance or very high transconductance is required a unipolar–bipolar interface is necessary. The circuit in figure 5.18 is an example of this, in which the p-channel MOS transistor is followed by an n–p–n, bipolar emitter follower. The upper MOS device in the figure is used as the load of the lower one. A number of these circuits can be fabricated on a single semiconductor chip.

Summary

This chapter has been concerned with the different logical systems which are currently available, and to enable the systems engineer to compare them, so that the appropriate choice can be made for any particular application. To assist in this, table 5.3 compares some of the characteristics of logical systems, and table 5.4* shows some typical, commercially available elements.

Table 5.3

System	Fan-out	Speed	Noise immunity	Comments
TRL	Fair	Slow	Good	Thin-film technique only
DCTL	Limited	Very fast	Good	Current-hogging problems
RCTL	Fair	Fair	Fair	Suitable for large chips
DTL	Good	Fast	Very good	Capable of two-level logic
TTL	Good	Very fast	Fair	Modified form preferred
CML	Very good	Very fast	Good	Dual-function output
CTL	Very good	Fast	Fair	Wired 'or' facility.

* On page 74.

Table 5.4

System	Manufacturer	Type no.	Fan-out max.	Speed (ns)	Logic levels '0'	'1'	Power dissipation (mW)	Supply Voltage (V)
DCTL	Fairchild	μL 915	5	12	0·15	1·0	24	3·0
DCTL	Westinghouse	PL 914	5	12	0	0·8	24	3·0
RCTL	Texas	SN 5161	5	65	2·0	0·3	2	3·6
RCTL	Raytheon	RC 1243	5	20	0·2	1·0	15	3·0
DTL	Westinghouse	WM 506	10	10	0·4	1·8	57	9·5
DTL	Sprague	UC 1001B	4	12	0·4	5·8	35	6, −3
TTL	Transitron	TNG 3041	20	10	0·2	3·0	15	5·6
TTL	Fairchild	TTuL 103	15	25	0·3	4·0	25	5·0
CML	Motorola	MC 309	26	6	−1·55	−0·75	49	−5·0
CML	Westinghouse	WS 371	25	10	−1·6	−0·8	220	−5·0

CHAPTER 6

Bistable Elements

RS* bistable elements

The counting and memory circuits of logical machines require elements which can be set into one of two states, and which will remain in the selected state until it is desired to reset the element to its other state. The element must then remain in the reset state until it is set again. An electronic circuit must therefore be devised which has two stable states, and for this reason a circuit of this kind is said to be a bistable element.

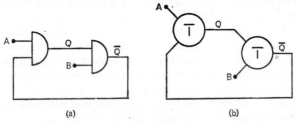

(a)   (b)

Figure 6.1

Two TRL elements can be used to form a bistable element as shown in figures 6.1a and 6.1b. The two figures show the same interconnection but using (a) the Old American Standard and (b) the British Standard logic symbols.

The bistable element itself forms a modular unit which is not only useful but essential to logical circuitry. The interconnection pattern between the two circuits in the figure may be laid down on the protective oxide coating of a silicon chip or as a part of a thin film circuit.

* Reset-set (see appendix B).

In figure 6.1, the inputs, A and B, can be used to set the element into either of its two states, as indicated at the output terminals, Q and Q̄.

There are three important ways in which the state of a bistable element may be changed. The first of these is by changing the direct voltage levels, at A and B in the figure. Here, if A takes up the more positive level, or B goes negative, the output of the bistable element at Q will be at the more negative level. Thus, the level taken up at Q is different from that of A and the same as that of B. For this reason, A is called the direct reset terminal of the element and B is the direct set terminal. Diodes are sometimes included, so that the bistable element is affected by certain voltage levels only, or to limit the voltage excursion of the outputs.

Secondly, the change of state may be brought about by pulses, perhaps derived from the voltage edge produced at the output of some other, similar element, when it changes state. In the logical diagram of figure 6.1, we are given no information about the nature of the active devices. For example, a positive-going pulse may be used to turn on an n–p–n transistor, or a negative-going one to turn it off. It is usually the case that the logical designer wishes to use only one of these types of pulse. Here again, diodes are used, and the unwanted pulses are suppressed. A typical circuit which illustrates some of these features is shown in figure 6.2.

Because provision has been made for direct level and pulse setting, the circuit is now rather different from that of the original concept of TRL, previously considered. Its construction is particularly suitable for a hybrid technique using a deposited layer of metal on silicon oxide for the capacitors, and the diodes, transistors, and resistors produced by diffusion in the silicon layer below the oxide. 'Speed-up' capacitors can also be included across the coupling resistors which link the two transistors in the bistable pair. All capacitors are, of course, expensive in terms of chip area, and should be avoided as much as possible.

In addition, the circuit shows two emitter followers. These increase the fan-out from about 5 to perhaps 25.* The circuit of figure 6.2, is intended for use with negative logic, so that, for instance, a negative

* An output circuit of this sort is used in the Texas SN 511.

level, i.e. a '1' at R_D, would forward bias the two diodes associated with the right-hand transistor in the figure, turning off this transistor, to yield a '0' at $\bar{Q}$. A similar result can be obtained with a negative-going edge or pulse at R. If, alternatively, S and R are joined, then the direct level inputs can be used to route pulses from this common point, to set or reset the bistable element. The operation of bistable elements where these points are connected will be discussed later.*

A third method of controlling a bistable element, sometimes known as 'pull-down', is to force the collector level to change. If a

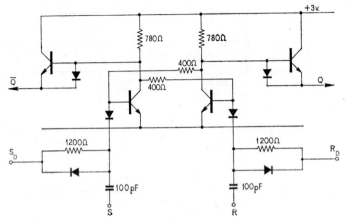

Figure 6.2

transistor, one-half of a bistable pair, is not conducting, its potential level will be that of the supply line. If then some other circuit, attached to the collector, be made to become heavily conducting, the collector potential will fall almost to zero, turning off the other transistor in the bistable pair, and so causing the first one to conduct. The external circuit which pulls the collector down need only pass current momentarily, so this is only a form of pulse operation. It should also be noticed that it is necessary for this trigger¦ circuit to be off, in its rest condition, and to be pulsed into conduction. With n–p–n

* See pages 82 and 103.

devices, this will usually mean that positive levels and positive-going pulses will be required if they are to be applied to the bases of transistors. A typical circuit of this kind is shown in figure 6.3. The design of this circuit is based on the DCTL gates discussed in chapter 5. It is typical of the earlier, integrated circuit designs.

Since all of these circuits are produced by integrated techniques, the concept of the individual component is not entirely appropriate, except for historical reasons, and the role of the component in integrated electronics must be rather akin to that of the a.c. equivalent

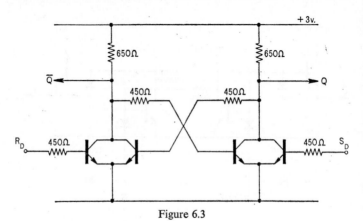

Figure 6.3

circuit in discrete circuitry. It is a model which helps us to understand better the performance of the circuit, but we should not expect to find that the appearance of the circuit is at all like that of the model. It is for this reason that the use of circuit symbols is bound to be important. This must be the case with linear amplifiers as well as with logical elements. The mechanism of the circuit is neither more nor less interesting to the systems engineer than was the theory of thermionic emission to the radio engineer of years ago. The circuits he used depended upon it, but, once understood, it did not hold the centre of his interest.

The logical symbol must remind us of the limitations of the basic element. In the case of bistable elements, the British Standard symbol is shown in figure 6.4. The convention which is adopted here is that all inputs, whatever their nature, which cause the element to be set, producing a '1' at the output, Q, are shown on the opposite side of the same square as Q, whilst resetting inputs are shown on the $\bar{Q}$ half of the symbol. This figure has been lettered to correspond with that of figure 6.2.

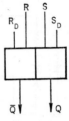

Figure 6.4

The circuit of figure 6.3 was based on a DCTL system, and the circuit of figure 6.2, although derived from TRL, has some points in common with DTL elements. This may serve to illustrate the fact that the development of electronic circuits has passed through a number of stages in which the new techniques are much influenced by earlier methods. Thus, at one time, the influence of valve circuitry on transistor circuit design was very marked. In this figure, the influence of discrete circuitry is still apparent. Later developments, as will be seen here, show a far more economic utilisation of the surface area of semiconductor chips.

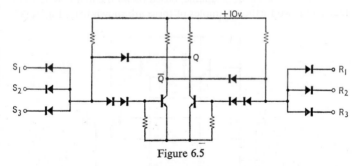

Figure 6.5

Figure 6.5 shows a typical, DTL bistable element, based on cross-coupled DTL elements. In this circuit, there are more active elements, such as diodes and transistors, which take up less surface area, a reduction in the number of resistors, and the complete elimination of capacitors.

This circuit has all the conventional advantages of DTL; a high supply voltage and good immunity to noise voltages, as well as a good fan-out. Fan-out can be further increased by using isolating stages, as shown in figure 6.6. This is, however, at the expense of chip area as further resistors now become necessary.

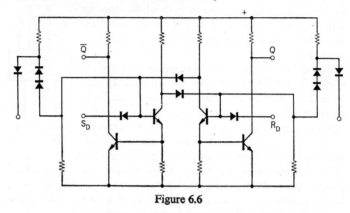

Figure 6.6

Bistable elements are available, based on all the major systems of logic, and two further examples of these are shown here. Figure 6.7

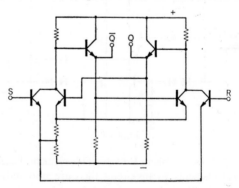

Figure 6.7

shows a bistable element which is operated in the current mode. Circuits such as this are developed to be compatible in speed and logic levels with other logical elements. Thus, the CML bistable element is intended for use with the somewhat inconvenient logic levels of CML gates.

Unlike the CML elements described in chapter 5, there is no need for a reference potential in the bistable element. Since the CML bistable element is intended for use in a system with other CML gates, the input levels at the set and reset terminals are not sufficient to cause saturation of the transistors. This is partly due to the reference potential associated with these other gates.

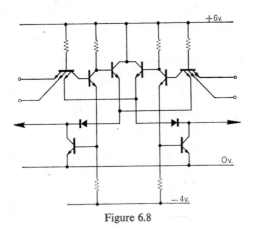

Figure 6.8

The TTL bistable element shown in figure 6.8 uses multiple emitter transistors as 'or' gates, operating in the common-base mode. The cross-coupling is isolated from the input by using separate emitters for this purpose. Each cross-coupling chain includes an emitter follower, so that the loading of one-half of the element on the other does not limit the operating speed of the element. Separate stages are also used to isolate the bistable element from its load.

Typical values for the supply lines are quoted, so that readers can see that this circuit is typical of TTL, with its good separation of logic levels.

RST* bistable elements

All these bistable elements are intended to be operated in the set–
reset manner, in which pulses or direct voltage levels on the inputs
are used to set the state of the output of the element. It was suggested,
in connection with the circuit of figure 6.2, that an integrated bistable
element could be devised in which input pulses could be routed from
one common point to switch the element. This routing path is determined by external voltage levels applied to the circuit.

Thus, in figure 6.2, if S and R are connected, and pulses applied
to this connection, the voltage levels at S_D and R_D decide whether
the pulses are routed to the left-hand or right-hand transistor. This

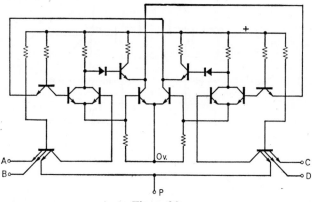

Figure 6.9

is because it is possible to isolate either of the transistors by reverse
biasing the appropriate input diode. Bistable elements which are
intended to be operated by a single trigger or pulse line are said to
be RST elements. In addition, the element in figure 6.2 could be
called an externally gated element, since the routing was in that
case determined by conditions external to the element.

Figure 6.9 shows a more sophisticated, RST bistable element, the
design of which is based on TTL elements. The inputs, A, B, C, and
D, are responsible for setting and resetting the element. The switch-

* Reset–set trigger (see appendix B).

ing pulses are applied at the point, P, simultaneously to both sides of the element.

The transistors which form the bistable pair are in the centre of the figure, and, if the right-hand of these is conducting at some instant, a pulse applied at A or B will cause current to flow in the input transistor on the left of the figure. This will bias into con- duction the transistor connected to its collector, so cutting off the transistor with which it is in parallel. This initiates a cumulative action, the result of which is that the element changes state.

JK* bistable elements

As the speed of operation of bistable elements increases with newly developed circuitry, so that, when pulses are applied, they are separated by very short time intervals, it becomes increasingly likely that with natural delay elements (for instance, the inductance of a straight wire), pulses will be applied very nearly simultaneously to both sides of a bistable element. When pulses are applied to the P input in figure 6.9, the routing will determine the state of the element. However, some RS elements have no routing. Figure 6.3 shows an example of this. Alternatively, in figure 6.2, if S_D and R_D are both negative, the element becomes capable of passing pulses from both S and R.

If then, negative-going pulses are applied simultaneously to these inputs, it is not possible to forecast the state which the element will take up. This is often expressed in the form of a truth table. The table 6.1 shown here refers to the figure, and is drawn up for negative logic, and for similtaneous inputs to S and R.

Table 6.1 *Truth table for a RS bistable element*

S_D	R_D	Q_{n-1}	Q_n
0	0	0	0
0	1	0	0
1	0	0	1
1	1	0	uncertain
0	0	1	1
0	1	1	0
1	0	1	1
1	1	1	uncertain

* See appendix B.

In this case the uncertainty occurs when both inputs are at the '1' level. Had positive logic been used, this would have occurred with both inputs at the '0' level. The JK bistable element overcomes this, since it is designed to ensure that the output after n pulses, Q_n, is inverted from the previous output, Q_{n-1}, in this condition of uncertainty. Thus, in negative logic, it could be said that for a JK element, $Q_n = \overline{Q_{n-1}}$, when $S_D = R_D = 1$.

The JK element has been defined as a bistable element which always changes state when a clock pulse is applied and its set and reset guides are at the '1' level. However, this definition presupposes a particular logic convention. Thus, it is better to define it as a bistable element in which there are no states of uncertainty in the output level due to any combinations of input levels.

The JK element was not easy to design in monolithic form, but it was early seen that, whereas its complexity would make it uneconomic in discrete form, silicon chip techniques make it a very desirable element. One reason for this is that a relatively small price has to be paid for the increased number of circuit components.

The truth table for a JK element is given in table 6.2. This table corresponds to the logical convention of table 6.1.

Table 6.2 *Truth table for a JK bistable element*

$J(S_D)$	$K(R_D)$	Q_{n-1}	Q_n
0	0	0	0
0	1	0	0
1	0	0	1
1	1	0	1
0	0	1	1
0	1	1	0
1	0	1	1
1	1	1	0

The action of a JK element can be investigated using a conventional bistable such as that shown in figure 6.2 and two 'nand' gates, shown here in figure 6.10 in American symbols.

The bistable element is used with two 'nand' elements whose outputs control the levels of the bistable routing gates. Since both these 'nand' elements only have a '0' level output, if both sets of inputs are at the '1' level, it is impossible with this arrangement for this to occur. Thus, pulses are always routed correctly, and, in particular, when R and S in figure 6.10 are both '1', the routing will be determined by the original state of the element, so that it changes state.

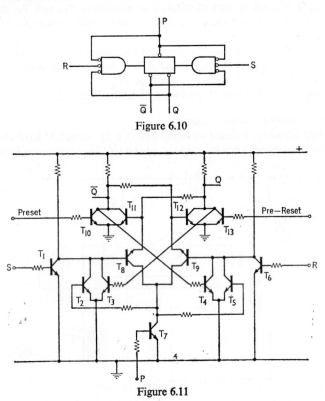

Figure 6.10

Figure 6.11

Figure 6.11 shows a typical integrated JK bistable element. The transistors, T_1, T_2 and T_3, correspond to a 'nand' gate in figure 6.10, and T_4, T_5, and T_6 to the other 'nand' gate, the transistors T_3 and T_4 sensing the initial state of the bistable element. T_7 is a pulse amplifier to give more rapid switching.

G

The level at the output of each input gate decides the state of the transistors T_8 and T_9. Only one of these transistors can be conducting at any time. When either of them is turned off, the charge which it releases is able to turn on the associated transistor, T_{11} or T_{12}, if it is off at that moment. The transistors T_{10} and T_{13} are used to set up the state of the element before pulses are applied to T_7.

Any JK element requires some form of internal memory, in this case that of charge storage. Other designs have used capacitors, or use of a master/slave bistable combination.

Some applications of these elements will be discussed in chapter 8.

MOS transistor bistable elements

MOS transistor bistable elements like that in figure 6.12 have also been developed. They have all the advantages associated with MOS

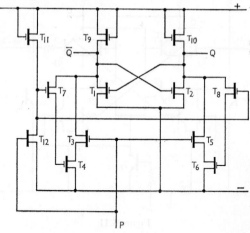

Figure 6.12

devices and, where a mixture of p-channel and n-channel devices are used, power requirements are very small, and limited to the duration of the transient period between the bistable states.

In figure 6.12, the basic bistable element consists of T_1 and T_2

loaded by T_9 and T_{10} acting as voltage-controlled resistors. T_7 and T_8 are steering elements for the clock pulses, and the two combinations T_3–T_4 and T_5–T_6 are 'and' gates controlled by the bistable logic levels and the clock pulse. T_{12} is an inverter loaded by T_{11}, which is used to drive T_7 and T_8 in antiphase with the clock waveform.

This bistable element, in common with other MOS devices, is relatively slow in operation and requires an interface* if other semiconductors are to be driven from it.

Logical applications of integrated circuits

Long before integrated electronic circuits had been developed, logical designers had evolved the concept of discrete components assembled on small chasses or printed cards to form building bricks for use in logical systems. Thus, much of the material for this chapter has already been directly stated in other books in this series,† or has been indirectly suggested elsewhere in this book. In particular, the ways in which 'nor' and 'nand' elements can be used to give physical meaning to Boolean functions are well known, and the introduction of integrated electronics has brought little new here, except for the obvious reduction in size and improvements in expectations of reliability.

However, the use of integrated electronics must result in a tendency to design powerful systems more often, using 'nor' (or 'nand') modules and bistable elements. Alternatively, at high speed, 'and-or' logic may be used in CTL systems.

The techniques for minimising Boolean expressions into a 'nor' or 'nand' form depend on whether or not the negations of the inputs are available. The following example shows the methods which may be employed.

$$f = \bar{A}\bar{B}\bar{C} + A\bar{B}\bar{C} + A\bar{B}C + \bar{A}\bar{B}C + \bar{A}BC + ABC \quad (6.1)$$

The function in equation (6.1) must first be minimised, for example by using the map method,‡ looping groups of cells as shown in table 6.3.

* See figure 5.18.
† In particular, 'An Introduction to Counting Techniques and Transistor Circuit Logic' by K. J. Dean.
‡ See appendix A.

Table 6.3

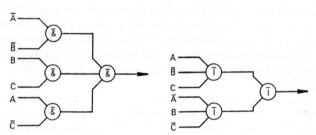

The minimal form of the function is thus

$$f = \bar{A}\bar{B} + BC + A\bar{C} \qquad (6.2)$$

This leads immediately to an 'and-or' logical system. It can also be directly converted to 'nand/nand' form as follows:

$$f = \overline{\overline{\bar{A}\bar{B}} \cdot \overline{BC} \cdot \overline{A\bar{C}}} \qquad (6.3)$$

The form of the function in equation (6.3) leads to the circuit shown in figure 6.13.

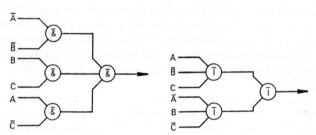

Figure 6.13   Figure 6.14

When designing a 'nor' network, it is better to loop groups of 0's rather than 1's on the map, or if this is not easily possible, as in this case, to write the expression in terms of 0's. Thus, the function in equation (6.2) may now be written down as

$$f = \overline{\bar{A}B\bar{C} + A\bar{B}C} \qquad (6.4)$$

Equation (6.4) can then be put into 'nor/nor' form as follows:

$$f = \overline{\overline{A + \bar{B} + C} + \overline{\bar{A} + B + \bar{C}}} \qquad (6.5)$$

This leads to the network shown in figure 6.14.

It will be seen that if the negations of the inputs are not available in figure 6.14, a total of six elements are necessary to operate the system. This number can often be reduced by a process of optimisation.* The function in equation (6.2) must be expressed in such a form as to reduce the number of negated inputs required. The method depends on a theorem that

$$(XY + Z) = (X + Z)(Y + Z)$$

When put into this form certain terms may be combined and others eliminated. In this example, the process is repeated until the optimum form is obtained.

$$f = \bar{A}\bar{B} + BC + A\bar{C} \qquad (6.2)$$
$$= (\bar{A}\bar{B} + B + A\bar{C})(\bar{A}\bar{B} + C + A\bar{C})$$

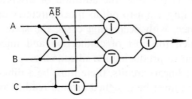

Figure 6.15

Note that terms such as $\bar{A} + A$ can be eliminated, being effectively replaced by 1.

$$f = (\bar{A} + B + A\bar{C})(\bar{A} + C + A\bar{C})(\bar{B} + C + A\bar{C})$$
$$= (\bar{A} + B + \bar{C})(A + \bar{B} + C) \qquad (6.6)$$
$$= (\bar{A}\bar{B} + B + \bar{C})(\bar{A}\bar{B} + A + C)$$

Equation (6.6) can then be realised as shown in figure 6.15.

* Zissos, D., and Copperwhite, G. W., 'Further Developments in the Design of Minimal NOR (and NAND) Combinational Switching Circuits for N-Variables' – *Electronic Engineering*, **38**, July 1966, p. 436.

CHAPTER 7
Linear Amplifiers

Introduction

When discussing digital circuits, it was seen that the design method was to devise a system which consisted entirely of silicon chips without, as far as possible, the addition of discrete components. Further, it was important to put as much circuitry on a single chip as possible, since, with decreasing costs, the state has now been reached in which the cost of connection and interconnection is greater than that of producing the silicon chip.

In the case of linear circuits, there must be a different approach. Here, the system must be designed around readily available amplifiers, comparators, etc. The performance of these elements must then be modified by discrete or thin-film components. Thus, wide-band amplifiers will often be used, the gain of which can be modified by external, negative feedback, and the frequency response of which can be adjusted by RC filters.

Thin-film amplifiers

Integrated amplifier circuits began to appear in the era when the chief attribute of integrated circuits was reliability rather than competitive costing with discrete amplifiers. Since then, the applications of linear integrated amplifiers have become more numerous, although the market trends are still largely set by digital circuitry. Thus the cost of integrated amplifiers has been slow to fall.

Differential amplifiers

Two types of amplifier have been popular in this connection; firstly the differential amplifier, such as that shown in figure 7.1, and, secondly, the wide-band amplifier, often directly coupled, whose characteristics can be modified by external, thin-film networks, or by discrete components.

The amplifier shown in figure 7.1 is typical of thin-film circuits, in that it uses a large ratio of passive to active components. The circuit is produced using cermets on an alumina substrate. The collector resistors are individually adjusted by the manufacturers to within 1 per cent. of the stated values. The transistors are flip chips, and the frequency response extends to 10 megahertz. The open circuit voltage gain is 40.

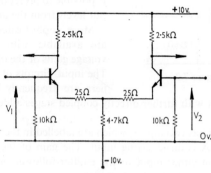

Figure 7.1

The design of this type of amplifier is aimed at reducing the differential offset voltage ($V_1 - V_2$), which is here 5 millivolts, and the incremental, base offset voltage due to temperature changes. This is $d(V_1 - V_2)/dT$ and is here 20 microvolts per °C over a temperature range in excess of 150°C.

The incremental, base offset voltage is bound to be small if the transistors are carefully matched, and if they both suffer identical temperature changes. This state of affairs is likely to exist in silicon chip circuits where the transistors are produced simultaneously by the same diffusions, and where they are very close together.

Silicon chip circuits

The differential amplifier in figure 7.2 is typical of silicon chip circuits. The ratio of passive to active elements has been decreased, and, owing to the silicon chip construction, the incremental, base offset voltage has been reduced, being nearly zero at 60°C and not exceeding 10 microvolts per °C over a range of 150°C. Access to the base of the transistor, T_3, enables the output voltage level to be adjusted, and emitter degeneration to be introduced, so controlling the voltage gain and making it possible to preset the direct output levels from the amplifier.

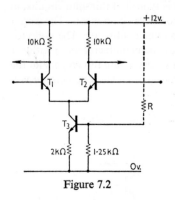

Figure 7.2

More sophisticated amplifiers are available with open-circuit voltage gains of the order of 5000. The input circuits of such amplifiers are frequently like that in figure 7.2, but with further directly coupled stages added, as shown in figure 7.3.

This circuit has two inputs, which are labelled in the figure A and Ā, of which Ā is an inverting input. The gain of the amplifier is the same from either input to the emitter-follower output. High-gain amplifiers with this kind of circuit arrangement are used as operational amplifiers and are the basis of summing and integrating amplifiers in analogue computers. One of the requirements in analogue computer design is that the amplifiers should have as near zero offset voltage as possible. It is also necessary to minimise amplifier drift in voltage levels. Using integrated circuits, analogue computers can be designed and constructed to solve specific problems in difficult environments, such as airborne autopilots and missile guidance controllers. The inherent advantages of integrated electronics can be employed to produce amplifiers which are more stable than discrete transistor circuits, without some of the precautions which accompany those circuits. One example of this is the necessity for inserting the discrete transistors into holes in a large copper block to act as a thermal stabiliser.

The resistor–capacitor combination in figure 7.3 is applied externally, and provides frequency compensation, so that a predetermined frequency-gain specification can be achieved. Circuits which are flexible as regards modification of gain and other characteristics are likely to sell in larger quantities than those where such components are integral parts of the circuit. Thus, the cost of development and of producing the original masks is more rapidly recovered. Hence, the price of the article falls. The silicon chip circuit in plate 6 is that of a high-gain amplifier. Note the relative

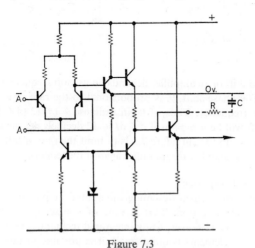

Figure 7.3

surface area taken up by capacitors, resistors, and transistors. There are also some extra components included for test purposes. The leads to the circuit have been wedge bonded.

Figure 7.4 shows symbolically an amplifier with open-loop voltage gain, A. A fraction, β, of its output is fed back to the inverting input. The voltage gain with feedback is $v_o/v_i = A/(1 - \beta A)$, where β is defined so that, with negative feedback, the feedback factor, βA, is negative. Hence, the feedback network (and also the frequency compensation) can be isolated from the input signal. This is, of course, a simplified view of the circuit, since, at high frequencies, it cannot be assumed that the phase shift of the amplifier is constant, nor that of the phase-shifting network.

In figure 7.5, the feedback factor is $(R_2A)/(R_1 + R_2)$. It is always necessary to ensure that under these conditions, where the phase shift of the feedback factor is $180°$, the factor will be less than unity.

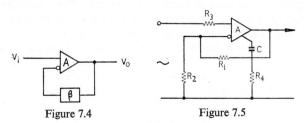

Figure 7.4   Figure 7.5

The phase shift of an amplifier depends on its gain-frequency characteristic. The phase shift, θ, is proportional to the rate of change of gain with frequency. Thus, if θ (in radians) $= (\pi/12)(\mathrm{d}A/\mathrm{d}f)$, the phase shift will be π radians if $\mathrm{d}A/\mathrm{d}f = 12$ decibels per octave. The purpose of C and R_4 in figure 7.5 is to limit the rate of fall of gain, $\mathrm{d}A/\mathrm{d}f$, and so stabilise the amplifier against the tendency to oscillate.

Common-mode rejection

One of the problems in designing differential amplifiers is that of common-mode rejection. This is not, of course, peculiar to integrated circuits. However, using integrated techniques in which the cost of active elements is quite small, it is possible to take special precautions to minimise it.

The common-mode rejection, p, of a circuit may be defined by the equation

$$v_{op}\, p = v_{ip}\, a_v$$

where v_{op} is the output error voltage, a_v is the voltage gain of the amplifier, and v_{ip} is the common-mode input voltage which when applied to both the direct and inverting inputs results in the output voltage, v_{op}. It is usual to measure $\log p$ in decibels, a typical value being 60 decibels.

The common-mode rejection of an amplifier is a function of its gain-frequency characteristic, since, at high frequencies, the parasitic capacitances of the silicon chip play an increasing part in determining the limit of the ability of an amplifier to reject common-mode voltages. The performance of an amplifier is improved when there is no impedance mismatch between the inputs. Thus, there must be impedances of similar value from the common line to each of its inputs.

The transistor T_3 in figure 7.2 and the corresponding transistor in figure 7.3 were included to increase the rejection of common-mode voltages. In figure 7.3, the zener diode clamped the base-emitter voltage of this transistor against common-mode voltages.

Wide-band amplifiers

All the amplifiers examined have been differential amplifiers. The applications of this type of amplifier depend on its wide band characteristics and its direct coupling, so that its response extends from zero frequency to some high frequency, and is linear over a very wide range. Such amplifiers are very useful as detectors, but the

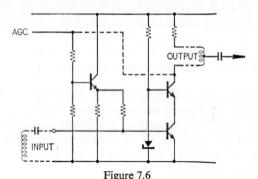

Figure 7.6

linearity of amplification is only very good for small signals of the order of a few millivolts. Another range of wide-band amplifiers is intended to be indirectly coupled or the amplifiers themselves contain indirect coupling. It is intended that the response of such amplifiers should not only be modified by selective feedback, but that tuning with resonant circuits, either with lumped components or by quartz or ceramic elements, should be used to obtain desired response curves.

Figure 7.6 shows a typical video amplifier based on a cascode circuit in which the base current of the input transistor of the cascode pair is controlled by the AGC* emitter follower. In the event of AGC not being used, this input may be connected, as shown by the broken line in the figure, to the collector of the output transistor. The zener diode ensures that this transistor is driven as a common-base stage.

Amplifiers of this kind are available, operating at up to several hundred megahertz. One of these, typical of this kind of circuit, the Philco 713, has a power gain of 11 decibels at 200 megahertz. It is at these higher frequencies where parasitic capacitances are most important. Hence, in order to maintain amplifier performance, hybrid, thin-film and multi-chip circuits have been frequently employed for high frequencies. Thus, a typical, thin-film, amplifier substrate operating at 100 megahertz and having a gain of 20 decibels might have two Kovartab or flip chip transistors, five capacitors, and nine resistors. This sort of ratio would not be acceptable for silicon chip circuits, where the capacitances associated with isolation lands have to be kept small. For example, resistance values must be as low as possible, so that they are not shunted by low capacitive reactances. This applies also to any feedback resistors used in stabilisation networks.

Other techniques in the design of tuned, integrated amplifiers have included the use of quartz and ceramic filters. When a piezo-electric resonator is solidly mounted on a substrate, acoustic energy is coupled to the substrate. To avoid this, the resonator must be mounted on a series of mismatching layers of alternately high and low acoustic impedance.

Voltage regulators

One of the obvious applications for integrated electronics which has been taken up by a number of manufacturers is as voltage regulators. Conventional power supplies for discrete transistor and integrated circuits are stabilised by amplifying changes in the output supply voltage, and using this to control the current through the series regulator which is a part of the power supply system. A circuit of this kind is shown in figure 7.7. The differential amplifiers con-

* Automatic Gain Control.

sidered earlier in the chapter are not primarily designed for this type of application.

The circuit shown in the figure is that of a simple regulator amplifier. The parts of the figure which are joined by broken lines are additional to the integrated circuit. The series power regulator, T, may be called upon to dissipate considerable power, and is thus less suitable for inclusion on a single chip than are the low-power elements of the differential amplifier.

The amplifier shown in the figure is extremely simple, consisting

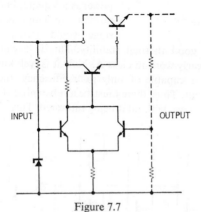

Figure 7.7

of a differential pair whose output is coupled by an emitter follower into the external series regulator. In order to obtain an extremely low stabilisation factor, and consequently a low output impedance from the power supply, a more sophisticated amplifier than this is required and also a Darlington combination of emitter followers. The availability of this kind of circuit is very likely to increase in the future.

FET's in amplifiers

The compatibility of field effect transistors and planar transistors in integrated circuits has resulted in the development of amplifiers which have FET input circuits, coupled to planar transistor amplifiers. An example of this is shown in figure 7.8. The circuit is that of an audio amplifier, which is driven from a crystal pick-up.

The input to the circuit is a p-channel FET, and an FET device acts as its load. Its high slope resistance is an example of one way of obtaining high values of load in integrated circuits. The high output impedance of the FET is matched to the output transistor by a Darlington pair. The final transistor is a small power transistor. For many domestic applications, a few milliwatts of power is adequate, but, where higher powers are employed, this power stage would need to be separately mounted for good thermal stability. This is because the output stage must clearly work in class A. Now it is well known that class A operation is capable of only poor efficiency, theoretically less than 50 per cent. Thus, there must be a substantial standing current in this power stage, without it being saturated. This high dissipation

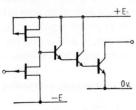

Figure 7.8

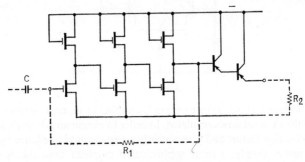

Figure 7.9

of power can be reduced if recourse is made to the more efficient class B operation (typically over 70 per cent. efficient), but this would require some phase-splitting circuitry in addition.

Low-power amplifiers are much more suitable for integrated circuitry, and devices are already appearing which consist almost entirely of FET and MOS arrays. An example of this is shown in figure 7.9.

The circuit is that of an audio amplifier, coupled to its load, R_2, by the p–n–p Darlington pair. Stabilisation of the operating point depends on the feedback resistor, R_1, and its frequency response depends both on R_1 and the input capacitor, C. Typical values of C and R_1 are 0·02 microfarads and 18 megohms. This type of amplifier is particularly suitable for deaf-aid applications.

Similar circuits to that shown in figure 7.9, except that two stages of MOS amplification would be required, can be used as pulse generators, the resistor, R_1, being replaced by a capacitor. Similar circuits have also been devised in which the feedback is arranged by a CR network, in which the 'resistive' elements are MOS devices. They are 'tuned' by adjusting their common gate potential.

The development of planar transistor and FET integrated amplifiers has undoubtedly lagged on that of digital circuits, and, in this field, expanding markets will undoubtedly provide the impetus to increase greatly the range of circuits now available.

Oscillators

One obvious application of linear integrated circuits is as a stable oscillator. When designing an oscillator which consists of an amplifier and a suitable phase-rotating network, it is essential, in

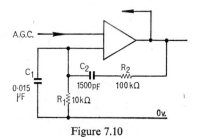

Figure 7.10

order to achieve low distortion, to arrange for the loop gain to be exactly unity when the device is operating in a linear mode. This problem of balance between amplifier gain and network attenuation cannot be easily solved by adjusting the network elements, since any change in parameters with temperature will result in imbalance. One solution is to use an AGC circuit to hold the gain at the level which is necessary to sustain oscillations.

In figure 7.10, when $R_1C_1 = R_2C_2$,

$$f_{res} = 1/(2\pi R_1 C_1)$$

Here $\qquad\qquad f_{res} = 1 \text{ kHz}$

The attenuation of the network must be less than the gain of the amplifier. The AGC line is then adjusted to hold the attenuation of the network and the gain of the amplifier in balance.

CHAPTER 8

Applications of Bistable Elements

One distinctive feature of the new electronics is the design of systems the building bricks of which are integrated circuits and not constructed with discrete components. Resulting from this trend is the use of the JK flip-flop as a universal bistable element. Before the introduction of integrated electronic circuits, it was seldom economically possible to use this type of element. This chapter will, therefore, be concerned particularly with examining the ways in which this element can be used and with emphasising those aspects of counter and shift register design which use those features which are especially characteristic of the JK type of bistable element.

JK flip-flop

The JK flip-flop was defined in chapter 6 as a bistable element which has output states which are unambiguous, whatever its input states might be. In particular, it is often stated that, if both the

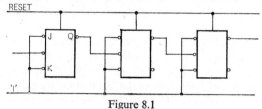

Figure 8.1

'setting' and 'resetting' inputs are at the 1 level, the next clock pulse will cause the element to change state. It is for this reason that the terms 'setting' and 'resetting' are not really appropriate for this element. They are therefore known as the J and K inputs, with the J input replacing the 'setting' terminal.

There are two important points to note. Firstly, if the J and K inputs are both taken permanently to the 1 level, then the flip-flop acts as though it were a T-type bistable element, because it will toggle each time an input pulse is received. This is what is required for a simple binary counter, such as that shown in figure 8.1.

Ripple counters

Many counters, such as that shown in figure 6.11, also have preset and pre-reset inputs. In this way, the general reset line can be used as shown in the figure, and the elements of the counter set up to some predetermined state. The counter shown in figure 8.1 is a typical ripple counter. It is so named because a change in the state of the first element may, under certain conditions, cause subsequent changes in later elements, so that a carry 'ripples' through the counter.

The second important point is concerned with the nature of the JK flip-flops which are commercially available. Some JK flip-flops have a pulse input and J and K inputs. For example, the TRL range of SGS-Fairchild elements are so specified in negative logic. In positive logic, these inputs are usually described as $\bar{J}$ and $\bar{K}$. When designing a counter, the logical input conditions for each stage of the counter must be discovered as part of the design process. If these are only known in either positive or in negative logic, and they must be found in the other logical convention, then this can be done by negating the known conditions. Some examples of this technique will be quoted later.

Where there are two J and two K inputs, one J input is joined to one K input, and it is to this combination that the clock pulses are applied. The same thing is true if there are two $\bar{J}$ and two $\bar{K}$ inputs. The significance of $\bar{J}$ and $\bar{K}$ lie in the fact that the logical convention that is used to define the JK bistable element is not the one which is used for the element when it is part of a counter. This change of definition is necessary if the JK flip-flop is also defined as changing state when a 1 is applied to whatever pulse input the element possesses. Thus, there are a number of elements which are available commercially which require distinctly different treatment in counter design. This will be illustrated by practical examples in this chapter.

Table 8.1 shows the truth table for a JK flip-flop with two J inputs and two $\bar{\text{K}}$ inputs, where one of each of these is used as a static input. Direct voltage levels are applied to them. The other inputs are connected and used dynamically for the clock pulse.

Table 8.1

J	$\bar{\text{K}}$	C	Q_{n+1}
X	X	0	Q_n
0	1	1	1
1	0	1	0
1	1	1	Q_n
0	0	1	$\bar{Q}_n$

When using this kind of flip-flop (e.g. Motorola MC 308) as a simple, binary ripple counter, the pulse input must be taken from the $\bar{\text{Q}}$ output of each element to provide pulses for subsequent stages. In this case, the remaining J and $\bar{\text{K}}$ inputs will be taken to the '0' level.

One of the advantages of this type of element is the ease with which it can be modified by feedback to provide ripple counters for any desired modulo, as shown in figure 8.2.

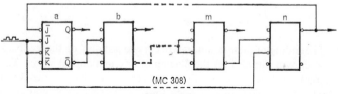

Figure 8.2

The counter operates in normal binary code until the elements a to m are all in the '1' state. This requires 2^{n-1} successive states including the all '0' state. The next count resets the elements a to m, and sets the flip-flop n so that there is a '1' fed back to the J input of flip-flop a. The next input pulse is thus unable to set this element or any of the following ones, but the input line which is taken directly to a $\bar{\text{K}}$ input of flip-flop n resets it, so regaining the all '0' state and removing the inhibit from flip-flop a. There are thus $2^{n-1} + 1$ counts in one complete cycle of the counter.

This kind of feedback counter should be compared with feedback counters formerly encountered which used RS flip-flops. In those cases, a feedback loop from the final stage of the counter to the first enabled the counter to skip one count in its binary sequence, so that instead of, say, 2^n counts, it gave $2^n - 1$ counts in a complete sequence.

By combining a feedback counter of the kind shown in figure 8.2 with an unmodified counter, it is possible to obtain almost any desired modulo. Some examples of this are given in table 8.2.

Table 8.2

Modulo	Unmodified counter stages	Feedback counter stages
2	1	0
3	0	2
4	2	0
5	0	3
6	1	2
7	–	–
8	3	0
9	0	4
10	1	3
11	–	–
12	2	2

The coding of these counters will depend not only on the feedback loop chosen but also on the placing of any unmodified stages. For example, a three-stage feedback counter which is preceded by a single, unmodified, binary stage forms a decade which counts in 8421 BCD, but, if instead it is followed by the unmodified stage, it counts in 5421 BCD.

These modulo-x counters are only possible if x satisfies the equation (8.1).

$$x = (2^{n-1} + 1)2^{m-n} \tag{8.1}$$

where there are m stages in the complete counter, and n of these are modified by feedback. From table 8.2, it can be seen that no integral solution is possible for n and m for certain values of x. These include 7, 11, 13, 19, and 23, and multiples of them. However, by using more than one feedback loop, it is possible to extend the operation of the counter to other moduli. An example of multiple feedback is shown in figure 8.3.

If the feedback loop from the flip-flop *d* is neglected at first, it will be seen that the counter consists of a modified counter with five states, followed by a single, unmodified binary stage, so that the

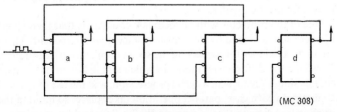

(MC 308)

Figure 8.3

complete counter would have ten states. However, the feedback from *d* to *b* modifies the last three stages, so omitting three states. Thus, the complete counter has three states less than the ten states previously deduced. Thus, the counter has seven states. It is weighted in 5421 code.

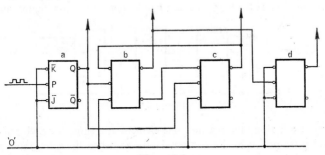

Figure 8.4

Where the flip-flops used have a single-pulse input, the circuits just described cannot be employed. Instead, it will be necessary to use a combination of feedback and feedforwards. An example of this is shown in figure 8.4.

The counter shown in this figure uses SGS-Fairchild Industrial range elements FμL 92329. It should be noticed that no inversion is needed to the pulse input so that as a simple binary counter each pulse input is driven from the Q output of the previous element. In the figure, there is a feedback loop from the flip-flop c to b, so that the overall counter has twelve states. Since it is unweighted, its main use is as a frequency divider.

One of the problems with all feedback counters is that their speed of operation is limited by the transient states that often occur. There are two techniques for increasing the speed of operation of counters. These are the shift register mode, in which all the bits in the register change simultaneously in a cyclic progression, and the use of clocked counters. In each case, parallel operation takes place, so limiting the propagation time to that of a single JK flip-flop, and, in some cases, the additional delay of a few logic gates.

Shift registers

The shift register in figure 8.5 is typical of the use of JK flip-flops as delay bistable elements, in which the input levels just prior to any clock pulse are transferred to the outputs of the same element one clock pulse later. Its simplest mode of operation is to supply digital information serially to the left-hand element in the figure and

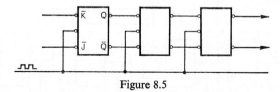

Figure 8.5

advance it along the register, one element at a time, for each pulse which is applied to the register. However, when the serial input is derived from the output of the register, the system is known as a circulating register or a ring counter.

A simple, decade ring counter consists of five elements, connected as in figure 8.5. The output from the Q terminal of the last element is applied to the J̄ terminal of the first. Similarly, Q̄ and K̄ are connected.

Circulating counters

This twisted ring counter is really one of the simplest logical arrangements of a series of circulating counters whose general input conditions are some function of the count stored in the register. As an example of the design procedure for this kind of counter, consider the sequence shown in table 8.3.

Table 8.3

A	B	C	Input conditions
0	0	1	1
1	0	0	1
1	1	0	1
1	1	1	0
0	1	1	0

This is clearly a circulating sequence. The method which will now be described is equally suitable for more sophisticated counters. However, when a sequence counter consists of more than four elements, there is the possibility that it might have more than one cyclic loop. Care must be taken to ensure that the counter always operates in the desired sequence. It is particularly likely that the incorrect sequence may be selected when the power supplies are switched on to the counter.

The method which will be used is the Karnaugh map method.*

From table 8.3, it can be seen that in the position '001' a '1' is the necessary input condition for the next count. This is because the next state in the cycle requires a '1' to be inserted at A. All the input conditions are shown in the table. First, the desired input conditions are registered on the Karnaugh map, and the remaining cells are assigned whatever conditions are necessary for minimisation. This is shown in table 8.4.

Table 8.4

* For an introduction to the use of Karnaugh maps see appendix A.

From the table, it can be seen that the minimised condition is $\bar{B} + \bar{C}$. This is the logical condition which determines the input level. A typical circuit of a counter which operates in this cycle is shown in figure 8.6.

A more detailed analysis of the kind described later in this chapter

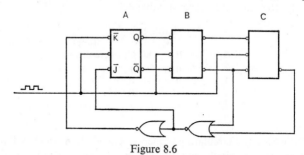

Figure 8.6

can be used to evolve separate input conditions for J and $\bar{K}$. It will then be found that, when these are minimised, the condition for J is B and for $\bar{K}$ it is $\bar{C}$. In this way, the use of gates can be avoided and the inputs to flip-flop A connected as just described.

Clocked counters*

The design of clocked counters follows a similar method, but it is more complex because input conditions are required for each of the flip-flops in the counter, whereas in the circulating counter the only input conditions which had to be ascertained were those for the first stage.

As a simple example, consider a scale-of-five counter which must operate in 421 code as shown in table 8.5.

Table 8.5

	A	B	C
0	0	0	0
1	0	0	1
2	0	1	0
3	0	1	1
4	1	0	0

* Also known as parallel counters or coherent counters.

The states which are represented on this table are then transferred to the Karnaugh map shown in table 8.6.

Table 8.6

C \ AB	00	01	11	10
0	0	2	x	4
1	1	3	x	x

At this point, the particular integrated circuits to be used must be selected. For example, if the SGS-Fairchild Fμl 92629 JK flip-flop is to be used, it is then possible to deduce the minimum necessary conditions to change the state of an element or to prevent it from changing state. These are shown for this element in table 8.7.

Table 8.7

State at clock time t	State at clock time $t+1$	J	$\bar{K}$
0	0	1	X
0	1	0	X
1	0	X	0
1	1	X	1

Then, using table 8.5, the input conditions for each of the flip-flops, A, B, and C, can be deduced, and from table 8.7 these can be written into two Karnaugh maps, one for each of the input conditions. This must be repeated for each flip-flop. The location of the

Table 8.8

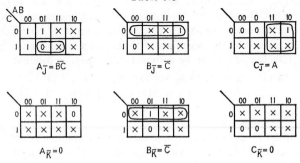

$A_J = \bar{B}\bar{C}$ $B_J = \bar{C}$ $C_J = A$

$A_{\bar{K}} = 0$ $B_{\bar{K}} = \bar{C}$ $C_{\bar{K}} = 0$

correct cells on the Karnaugh maps can be deduced from table 8.6. The completed maps are shown in table 8.8 and on them are shown the loops which are used to obtain the minimised input conditions. The complete counter is shown in figure 8.7.

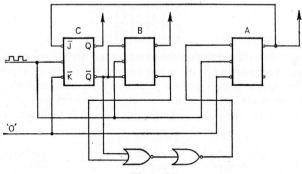

Figure 8.7

This type of treatment can be used to obtain a counter with any desired modulo, and any sequence or weighting. The analysis is entirely dependent on the truth table for the JK elements which are selected, and, as examples of the results which can be obtained, table 8.9 gives the input conditions for a number of differently coded decades using clocked counters.

The input conditions in table 8.9 are appropriate to a flip-flop which has $\bar{J}$ and $\bar{K}$ inputs and so on the transitions which are given in table 8.7. However, if a flip-flop is used which has inputs J and K but which is otherwise similar to that just described, the resulting conditions will be the negations of those given in table 8.9. Thus, a 8421 BCD counter can be designed with inputs as follows:

$$A_J = BCD; \quad A_K = D; \quad B_J = CD; \quad B_K = A + CD;$$
$$C_J = AD; \quad C_K = D; \quad D_J = 1; \quad D_K = 1.$$

Code conversion

Amongst the more obvious applications of bistable elements are examples of code conversion. Some of these are included here

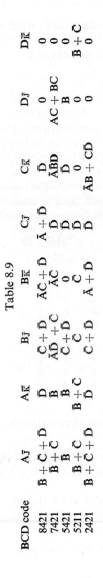

Table 8.9

BCD code	A_J	$A_{\bar{K}}$	B_J	$B_{\bar{K}}$	C_J	$C_{\bar{K}}$	D_J	$D_{\bar{K}}$
8421	$\bar{B}+C+\bar{D}$	$\bar{D}$	$C+\bar{D}$	$A\bar{C}+\bar{D}$	$\bar{A}+\bar{D}$	$\bar{D}$	0	0
7421	$\bar{B}+\bar{C}$	B	$\bar{A}\bar{D}+\bar{C}$	$\bar{A}C$	$\bar{D}$	$\bar{A}\bar{B}D$	$AC+BC$	0
5421	$\bar{B}$	$\bar{B}$	$C+\bar{D}$	0	$\bar{D}$	$\bar{D}$	B	0
5211	$\bar{B}+\bar{C}$	$B+\bar{C}$	C	C	$\bar{D}$	0	0	$\bar{B}+C$
2421	$\bar{B}+\bar{C}+\bar{D}$	$\bar{D}$	$C+\bar{D}$	$\bar{A}+\bar{D}$	$\bar{D}$	$\bar{A}B+C\bar{D}$	0	0

because their design is dependent on the use of JK flip-flops, and because they have only recently been developed specifically for systems which use integrated circuits.

Gray–binary conversion

Gray code is an example of a progressive code. It is used to avoid ambiguity in analogue to digital converters; for example, in digitising shaft position or linear movement. However, Gray code is not suitable for arithmetic operation, and so there are certain circumstances in which it must first be converted into binary code. Methods for conversion between Gray and binary codes which operate in a parallel mode are well known. The method suggested here uses a serial approach, in which there is some saving in the number of electronic circuits required when compared with parallel methods.

Table 8.10

Decimal	Gray code				Binary code			
	K	L	M	N	A	B	C	D
0	0	0	0	0	0	0	0	0
1	0	0	0	1	0	0	0	1
2	0	0	1	1	0	0	1	0
3	0	0	1	0	0	0	1	1
4	0	1	1	0	0	1	0	0
5	0	1	1	1	0	1	0	1
6	0	1	0	1	0	1	1	0
7	0	1	0	0	0	1	1	1
8	1	1	0	0	1	0	0	0
9	1	1	0	1	1	0	0	1

The rules for converting Gray code to binary code can be deduced from table 8.10.

(a) In both codes the most significant digits are always identical.
(b) Compare digits K and L. B is a 1 when K and L are non-equivalent.
(c) Compare B and M. C is a 1 when B and M are non-equivalent.
(d) Similarly compare C and N to obtain D. Repeat this process where there are further digits.

To show how this process can be carried out serially, consider the conversion of decimal 29 from Gray code to binary code as shown in table 8.11.

Table 8.11 *Conversion of decimal 29 from Gray code to binary code*

Binary code					Gray code					
A	B	C	D	E	J	K	L	M	N	
0	0	0	0	0	1	0	0	1	1	E and J non-equivalent, hence insert 1 at E and shift one place left.
0	0	0	0	1	0	0	1	1	0	E and J non-equivalent, insert 1 at E and shift.
0	0	0	1	1	0	1	1	0	0	E and J non-equivalent, insert 1 at E and shift.
0	0	1	1	1	1	1	0	0	0	E and J equivalent, insert 0 and shift.
0	1	1	1	0	1	0	0	0	0	E and J non-equivalent, insert 1 and shift.
1	1	1	0	1	0	0	0	0	0	stop.

From table 8.11, it can be seen that the problem consists chiefly in controlling the state of register element E, depending on its state and on the state of element J. All the remaining elements in the shift register are controlled in the usual way.

Now consider a JK flip-flop with inputs J and K as well as the clock pulse input. Its input conditions can be deduced from table 8.7 by taking the negations of the conditions there, or from table 8.12.

Table 8.12

State at clock time t	State at clock time $t + 1$	J	K
0	0	0	X
0	1	1	X
1	0	X	1
1	1	X	0

Table 8.13 shows all the possible states of elements E and J which lead to subsequent states of E.

Table 8.13

E_n	J_n	E_{n+1}
0	0	0
0	1	1
1	0	1
1	1	0

It is now possible to use the information in tables 8.12 and 8.13 to draw up maps from which the minimised input conditions for flip-flop E can be found. These are given in table 8.14.

Table 8.14

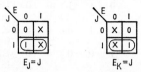

From table 8.14, it can now be seen that, to convert a number serially from Gray code to binary code, the inputs to the JK flip-flop E must be taken to the output of element J. The relevant part

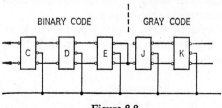

Figure 8.8

of the shift register is shown in figure 8.8. In addition, an 'and' gate must be arranged to stop the train of clock pulses when the contents of the register has been shifted out.

Binary–decimal converters

When converting from Gray code to binary code, the state of element E was found to be dependent on the state of element J. This was a very simple solution in this small logical system. The design problems are somewhat greater when converting a number from binary code into 8421 BCD. Such a system might form part of a decimal in-line read-out from a data processor.

Again, a serial converter will be designed, because the complexity of a serial decoder increases linearly with the number of digits being decoded, whereas a parallel system increases in complexity very sharply as the number of digits increases.

8421 BCD uses the first ten binary codes (including 0) to represent decimals 0 to 9. A second set is required to indicate tens and a third for hundreds. Hence, to convert a number such as 13 (binary code 1101) to 8421 BCD (code 10011), the filler required can be found by subtraction,

$$
\begin{array}{r}
1\,0\,0\,1\,1 \\
1\,1\,0\,1 \\
\hline
1\,1\,0
\end{array}
$$

In converting larger numbers, the interesting result is found that the difference may consist of the digits 11 (binary 3) and some number of 0's.

BCD 29 1 0 1 0 0 1	BCD 49 1 0 0 1 0 0 1
Binary 29 1 1 1 0 1	Binary 49 1 1 0 0 0 1
1 1 0 0	1 1 0 0 0
BCD 86 1 0 0 0 0 1 1 0	BCD 100 1 0 0 0 0 0 0 0 0
Binary 86 1 0 1 0 1 1 0	Binary 100 1 1 0 0 1 0 0
1 1 0 0 0 0	1 0 0 1 1 1 0 0

The rule appears to break down for numbers with more than two decimal digits until it is realised that the filler has been added more than once. The way in which this has been done can best be illustrated by a method similar to that shown in table 8.11. This will be the basis of the serial code converter.

From table 8.15, it will be seen that the number must be inserted into a shift register, and four stages of the register examined as the number is shifted left. When the number examined is equal to or greater than decimal 9, the filler is added. However, if the binary digits 11 are added instead of 110, as shown in table 8.16 some other difficulties are also avoided. The filler is now added to codes greater than 4.

Table 8.15

	A	B		
			1100100	Equals binary equivalent of decimal 100
		1	100100	
		11	00100	
		110	0100	
		1100	100	Add binary 110 and shift left
	10	0101	00	
	100	1010	0	Add binary 110 and shift left.
	1010	0000		Add binary 110 in column A
1	0000	0000		

Table 8.16

	A	B		
			1100100	Shift left
		1	100100	Shift left
		11	00100	Shift left
		110	0100	Add filler and shift left
	1	0010	100	Shift left
	10	0101	00	Add filler and shift left.
	101	0000	0	Add filler in column A and shift left
1	0000	0000		Stop

The complete converter therefore consists of a shift register which receives binary information and which is divided into groups of four elements, the combinational logic of which is so arranged that any state of the register depends on the state of certain elements in

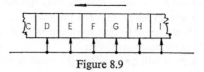

Figure 8.9

the register immediately previously. In this way, the controlled addition of the filler is carried out without the use of conventional adders. Instead, addition and shifting are carried out as the results of logically controlled processes which depend on the input conditions for each stage of the register. Table 8.17 shows all the possible states of the register and the subsequent states which must pertain. This table applies to the register shown in figure 8.9.

Table 8.17

States before shifting				States after shifting			
E	F	G	H	D	E	F	G
0	0	0	0	0	0	0	0
0	0	0	1	0	0	0	1
0	0	1	0	0	0	1	0
0	0	1	1	0	0	1	1
0	1	0	0	0	1	0	0
0	1	0	1	1	0	0	0
0	1	1	0	1	0	0	1
0	1	1	1	1	0	1	0
1	0	0	0	1	0	1	1
1	0	0	1	1	1	0	0

3 added (bracketing the last five rows of the "States after shifting")

States corresponding to greater than decimal 9 cannot occur, since such states would have been dealt with one shift pulse earlier.

Using the input conditions for a JK flip-flop described in table 8.12, Karnaugh maps can now be drawn up for the register elements D, E, F, and G. Two maps will be required for each of the elements. The minimised input conditions can then be deduced from these maps. The positions of the cells of these maps are shown in table 8.18.

Table 8.18

GH\EF	00	01	11	10
00	0	4	X	8
01	1	5	X	9
11	3	7	X	X
10	2	6	X	X

The remainder of the design procedure for the converter depends on the range of the logical elements which are avilable. Thus, if flip-flops with J and $\bar{K}$ inputs are used, the 0's and 1's on the maps in table 8.19 must be interchanged. If the logical conditions derived in table 8.19 must be obtained from 'nand' elements, then, remembering that a nand/nand system is equivalent to an and/or system, the

I

Table 8.19

gates can be sketched for the minimised conditions as shown in the example in figure 8.10.

If 'nor' elements are to be used for controlling the flip-flops, then, since a nor/nor system is equivalent to an or/and system, the minimised conditions must be put in or/and form, as shown in figure 8.11 for D_J.

$$D_J = E + FG + FH$$
$$= (E + F)(E + G + FH)$$

Care must however be taken to avoid redundancy when optimising nor/nor systems in this way. Consider, for example, the optimisation of G_J.

$$G_J = E\bar{H} + \bar{E}\bar{F}H$$
$$= (E + \bar{F}H)(\bar{E}\bar{F} + \bar{H})$$

It may not be immediately apparent that this may be reduced to

$$G_J = (E + H)(\bar{E}\bar{F} + \bar{H})$$

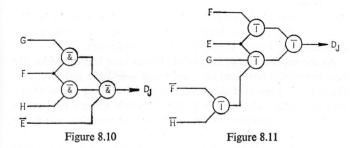

Figure 8.10   Figure 8.11

A useful method for finding convenient forms of the input equations in nor/nor form is to construct two Karnaugh maps, looping or shading groups of cells on each of the maps so that all the 1 states are included in the enclosed areas in each map. These groups *can* include 0 states so long as no 0 state is included on *both* of the maps.

Table 8.20

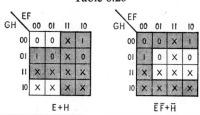

Table 8.20 shows how this may be done for G_J. It is interesting to note that this method not only shows quickly a simple form of the

expression, but it enables alternative forms to be quickly spotted. This may be of value in a system as complex as this, because the designer will be seeking overall optimisation, not merely minimisation of each input condition. Thus, some functions may be common to a number of shifting elements. Careful optimisation here may save a number of integrated circuits, and so avoid the problems of interconnecting them.

Conclusion

An attempt has been made in this chapter to show that the JK flip-flop is a universal bistable element, and that using it a wide variety of counters and other special circuits can be devised.

As the applications of integrated circuits have become wider, the new electronics has been accepted more quickly in industry. It is the author's hope that this book has explained his point of view – that the integrated circuit is to the electronic systems engineer in much the same position as the resistor or the capacitor was to the discrete circuit designer. If it has shown a little of the exciting panorama before the modern electronics engineer, it will have been well worth the effort.

APPENDIX A

Minimisation of Boolean Functions

The minimisation of Boolean functions is often discussed in text-books on logic, and when designing with integrated circuits it is an important topic. A certain amount of redundancy will often be left after minimisation, because any one range of integrated logical modules will usually have, for example, two- and four-input gates available, and these must be used for all the functions which must be produced. Conversely, there may be occasions on which the saving of one or more inputs could show considerable economies in the total number of integrated elements which are required.

The basic Boolean propositions are

$$A\bar{A} = 0$$
$$A + \bar{A} = 1$$
$$A0 = 0$$
$$A1 = A$$

and the two common forms of de Morgan's theorems are

$$\overline{A + B} = \bar{A}\bar{B}$$

and

$$\overline{AB} = \bar{A} + \bar{B}$$

There have been a number of methods put forward to minimise Boolean expressions, some of which are based on de Morgan's theorems. It is often true that these methods are tedious. Hence the quicker graphical methods such as the use of Veitch diagrams and Karnaugh maps are particularly valuable. The purpose of this appendix is to summarise the Karnaugh method for minimisation.

These maps show the method of approach for two, three, or four variables. The axes are labelled with a progressive code, actually Gray code, so that any cell on the map has adjacent cells in any direction which differ by only one binary digit.

121

The numbers written in the cells are the binary numbers which correspond to the code on the axes, written in the order ABCD,

Table A.1

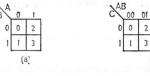

(a)

(b)

(c)

where A is the most significant digit. For example, the numbers 5, 7, and 15 have the codes 0101, 0111, and 111 respectively. Thus 5 and 7 share the common code $\bar{A}BD$, differing only in C, and 7 and 15 share the code BCD, differing only in A. This is the property of the map which is used in minimising Boolean expressions.

Consider the equation

$$Z = AB\bar{C}\bar{D} + AB\bar{C}D + \bar{A}\bar{B}CD$$
$$+ \bar{A}\bar{B}C\bar{D} + \bar{A}BCD + \bar{A}BC\bar{D} + A\bar{B}C\bar{D}$$

Wherever a term of this expression occurs on the map, a '1' is written and for all the remaining terms a '0' is written. Then groups of two, four, or eight terms are looped together until all the cells having the value '1' have been included. Any cell may be used in more than one loop. The map is then as shown in table A.2.

Table A.2

Note that it is quite satisfactory to loop together the terms $\bar{A}\bar{B}C\bar{D}$ and $A\bar{B}C\bar{D}$, since the opposite sides of the map are also progressively coded. It may be useful to consider that the left- and right-hand edges are joined, and also the top and bottom edges of the map.

Now by examining the map, it can be seen that the loop containing the terms $AB\bar{C}\bar{D}$ and $AB\bar{C}D$ can be simplified to $AB\bar{C}$, thus being reduced by one literal. The other loop of two terms similarly reduces to $\bar{B}C\bar{D}$. The loop which encloses four cells may at first be regarded as two horizontal loops enclosing two cells. These reduce to $\bar{A}CD$ and $\bar{A}C\bar{D}$, which, it can be seen, reduce further to $\bar{A}C$, so losing two terms in all. Loops of four always enable two literals to be discarded. Similarly, a loop of eight cells reduces to a single literal.

The minimised expression is thus

$$Z = AB\bar{C} + \bar{B}C\bar{D} + \bar{A}C$$

which can be reduced no further.

As a further example, consider a binary adder/subtractor for two digits A and B, whose sum S is $(A + B + C)$ and difference D is $(A - (B + C))$ where C is the carry or borrow from a previous addition or subtraction. The logic is

$$S = D = \bar{A}\bar{B}\bar{C} + \bar{A}B\bar{C} + \bar{A}\bar{B}C + ABC$$
$$C_s = AB\bar{C} + A\bar{B}C + \bar{A}BC + ABC$$
$$C_d = \bar{A}B\bar{C} + \bar{A}\bar{B}C + \bar{A}BC + ABC$$

C_s is the resulting carry when adding and C_d is the resulting borrow when subtracting. The minimisation is shown in table A.3.

Table A.3

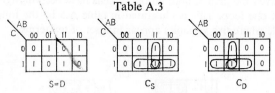

From table A.3, it can be seen that the table for the sum or difference cannot be further minimised, but that the functions for C_s and C_d can be simplified as follows:

$$C_s = AB + BC + AC$$
$$C_d = \bar{A}C + \bar{A}B + BC$$

It may be in some simplifications that there is a choice of looping
and it will be found that the most savings occur when groups of
eight are given precedence over groups of four, and groups of four
over groups of two. Thus, if a set of eight terms can be represented
on a Karnaugh map as shown in table A.4 there are a number of
alternative loopings which are possible. The minimisation produced
by each can then be compared with each of the others.

Table A.4

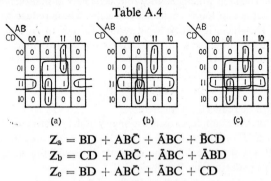

$$Z_a = BD + AB\bar{C} + \bar{A}BC + \bar{B}CD$$
$$Z_b = CD + AB\bar{C} + \bar{A}BC + \bar{A}BD$$
$$Z_c = BD + AB\bar{C} + \bar{A}BC + CD$$

From these results, it will be clear that there are less terms in the
minimisation produced by *c* than in either of the others.

When there are five variables, it is no longer possible to devise a
progressive coding for the axes. Instead, the map must be drawn in
two planes. Looping can then be carried out in either of the planes
or between the planes, until all the '1' cells have been brought into
at least one loop. This is illustrated in table A.5 by the following
example where five variables appear in a set of ten terms.

Table A.5

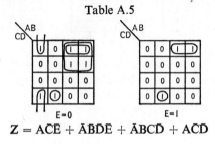

$$Z = A\bar{C}\bar{E} + \bar{A}\bar{B}\bar{D}\bar{E} + \bar{A}BC\bar{D} + A\bar{C}D$$

Expressions such as those just obtained are in the and/or form. They are suitable for use where and/or logic modules are available or when using nand modules, since the input to a two-stage nand/nand system can also be in this form. However, where nor modules are used, the function is better put in another form. This is because two stages of nor/nor logic are equivalent to an or/and logical system.

The necessary modification can be brought about if expressions, in the form $X + YZ$ are put as $(X + Y)(X + Z)$. This can be verified by truth table, or by the expansion

$$X + YZ = X + XY + YZ + XZ,$$

but $X + XY + XZ = X$, so that these additional terms can be eliminated.

For example, the expression for the carry, obtained previously, is in the correct form for and/or or nand/nand logic but must be modified as follows for nor/nor systems.

$$
\begin{aligned}
C_s &= AB + BC + AC \\
&= (A + BC + AC)(B + BC + AC) \\
&= (A + BC)(B + AC) \\
&= (A + B)(A + C)(B + C)
\end{aligned}
$$

similarly, $\quad\quad C_d = (\bar{A} + B)(\bar{A} + C)(B + C)$

and $\quad\quad S = D = (A + B + C)(A + \bar{B} + \bar{C})$
$$(\bar{A} + \bar{B} + C)(\bar{A} + B + \bar{C})$$

It will be seen here that these simple examples are extensions of de Morgan's theorems, but this is by no means always obvious.

APPENDIX B

Types of Bistable Element

This appendix sets out the main types of bistable element and distinguishes between them.

D flip-flop (delay bistable element)

This element has either a single input, D, or two inputs D and $\bar{D}$, and in addition a clock pulse input. The logic level at D appears at the output of the element one clock pulse later. Thus, if the output of the element is Q after n pulses and Q_1 after $n + 1$ pulses, its truth table is as shown in table B.1.

Table B.1

Q	D	Q_1
0	0	0
0	1	1
1	0	0
1	1	1

This element is used in shift registers and ring counters. One common form owes its properties to the external gating of its pulse-routing networks. It is these gates which are the D and $\bar{D}$ inputs. The capacitive pulse-routing inputs are joined and it is to these that the clock pulses are applied.

T flip-flop (trigger bistable element)

This element has a single input, T, and, when some given transition takes place, the output state of the element changes. The transition may be from the '0' to '1' level. The chief application of this element is as a simple binary counter. Because of its limitations, other types of element are often preferred.

126

RS flip-flop (reset–set bistable element)

This element has two inputs. When a '1' is put on the reset input, the output level changes to '0'. Similarly a '1' on the set input changes the output level to '1'. This type of element is controlled by direct current levels and so, if it is to be operated by clock pulses, external routing elements will be required. In addition, there is the provision that S and R must not be at the '1' level simultaneously. The truth table for the element is shown in table B.2.

Table B.2

R	S	Q	Q_1
0	0	0	0
0	1	0	1
1	0	0	0
1	1	0	X
0	0	1	1
0	1	1	1
1	0	1	0
1	1	1	X

X: Forbidden states leading to uncertainty in the state of Q_1.

Note: the positions of states of uncertainty in the truth table are a function of the logical convention employed.

RST flip-flop (reset–set trigger bistable element)

This bistable element has a trigger input which is often capacitively coupled, as in the T flip-flop, and also set and reset inputs which act as in the RS flip-flop. The provision which must be observed here is that not more than one of these three inputs shall be simultaneously at the '1' level. Its truth table is more complex than table B.2, owing to the larger number of inputs. There are four conditions leading to a '1' at Q_1, and eight conditions which are forbidden, since they lead to uncertainty in the state of Q_1.

JK flip-flop

The JK bistable element is usually defined as being similar to the RS flip-flop except that the state leading to uncertainty in the RS flip-flop is no longer forbidden. When both inputs are taken to the

'1' level, the output of the element always changes state. The J input corresponds to the S input in the RS flip-flop. Its truth table is shown in table B.3. It should be noted that there are now no input conditions which lead to uncertainty in the output states.

Table B.3

J	K	Q	Q_1
0	0	0	0
0	1	0	0
1	0	0	1
1	1	0	1
0	0	1	1
0	1	1	0
1	0	1	1
1	1	1	0

Many elements which are produced in integrated form are described as JK flip-flops, but they have often more than two input terminals. For example, two J and two K inputs may be provided. In such cases, one J and one K input may be joined and these then used as a T input. The Motorola MC 308 is an example of this, except that in that case the inputs are labelled $\bar{J}$ and $\bar{K}$.

It is still possible to regard these elements as JK flip-flops, except that the element was defined in a different logical convention. The SGS-Fairchild FμL 92329 is another example of an element with $\bar{J}$ and $\bar{K}$ inputs, except that here a clock input is also provided. The logic levels on the $\bar{J}$ and $\bar{K}$ inputs have no effect on the output level of the element until a clock pulse has been received. Table B.4 is a simplified truth table for the element in which the clock pulse conditions have been omitted.

Table B.4

J	$\bar{K}$	Q	Q_1
0	0	0	1
0	1	0	1
1	0	0	0
1	1	0	0
0	0	1	0
0	1	1	1
1	0	1	0
1	1	1	1

Bibliography

Materials and device technology

CAMPBELL, D. S. and BLACKBURN, H., 'The Characteristics of Thin Components' – Symposium at the Allen Clark Research Centre, March 1965.

DEAN, K. J., 'Transistors: Theory and Circuitry' – McGraw-Hill, 1964.

DICKEN, H. K., 'Monolith or Hybrid?' – *Electronic Design*, 17 Feb 1964, p. 66.

DUMMER, G. W. A., Conference at West Ham College of Technology, June 1963.

HARKNETT, M. R., 'Introducing MOST Devices' – *Electronics and Power* **12,** 3 Jan 1966.

IVESTAL, T. A., 'Basics of Integrated Circuit Components' – *Electronic Design*, 13 April 1964, p. 50.

KILBY, J. S., 'Silicon FEB Techniques' – *Solid State Design*, July 1964, p. 32.

LESK, I. A., 'Thin Film Hybrid Techniques' – *Solid State Design*, July 1964, p. 38.

NORMAN, R. H., 'Digital Applications of Integral Electronics' – *Solid State Design*, July 1964, p. 21.

SELIKSON, B. and LONGO, F. A., 'A Study of Purple Plague and its Role in Integrated Circuits' – *Proc. IEEE* **52**(12), 1964, p. 1638.

STERN, L., 'Basic Approaches to Integrated Circuit Design' – *Motorola Monitor* **2**(2), 1964, p. 6.

WEIMER, P. K., *et al.*, 'Integrated Circuits incorporating Thin Film Active and Passive Devices' – *Proc. IEEE* **52**(12), 1964, p. 1479.

Circuits

BOWES, R. C. and GRANVILLE, J. W., 'A 100 Mc/s Amplifier using Thin Film Integrated Circuits' – *Proc. IEEE* **52**(12), 1964, p. 1598.

DEAN, K. J., 'An Introduction to Counting Techniques and Transistor Circuit Logic' – Chapman & Hall, 1964.

FORTE, S., 'The Use of Semiconductor Integrated Circuit Building Blocks for Linear Electronic Systems' – IEE/IERE Symposium on Microminiaturisation, April 1964.

HUSKER, J. D. and POLLOCK, L. J., 'Diode Design boosts DTL Speed' – *Electronic Design*, Feb 1965, p. 36.

OLMSTEAD, J. A., 'Using MOS Transistors in Integrated Circuits' – *Electronic Design*, 27 April 1964, p. 80.

Systems and analytical methods

BISWAS, N. N., 'The Logic and Input Equations of Flip-Flops' – *Electronic Engineering* **38,** Feb 1966, p. 107.

BRIGHAM, R. C., 'Some Properties of Binary Counters with Feedback' – *IRE Trans.* EC-10, 1961, p. 699.

DEAN, K. J., 'The Design of Parallel Counters Using the Map Method' – *Proc. IEE* **32,** Sept 1966, p. 159.

DEAN, K. J., 'A Binary–Decimal Converter using Integrated Circuits' – *Electronic Engineering* **38,** Oct 1966, p. 662.

KARNAUGH, M., 'The Map Method for Synthesis of Combinational Logic' – *Communications and Electronics* **9,** Nov 1953, p. 539.

MARCUS, M. P., 'Cascaded Binary Counters with Feedback' – *IEEE Trans.* EC-12, 1963, p. 361.

MAXWELL, L., 'Synthesis of Counters with Any Kind of Feedback' – *Proc. IEE* **113,** Feb 1966, p. 271.

VEITCH, E. W., 'A Chart Method for simplifying Truth Functions' – *Proc. Assoc. Computing Machinery*, May 1952, p. 127.

WOOD, J. and BALL, R. G., 'Metal Oxide Semiconductor Transistors in Digital Logic and Storage' – *Proc. IERE* **32,** July 1966, p. 33.

Index

Items in bold type are included in the glossary (pages ix–xi)

131